ARRL's

HF DIGITAL HANDBOOK

Steve Ford, WB8IMY

Published by
ARRL—the national association for Amateur Radio
Newington, CT 06111 USA

CONTENTS

FOREWORD

As you read the first chapter of *ARRL's HF Digital Handbook*, you'll discover that the evolution of amateur HF digital communication has been nothing short of phenomenal—especially in recent years. Hams exploited RTTY after World War II and relied on it for decades to move text data throughout the world. Little changed until amateurs finally got their hands on affordable computer technology in the early '80s. HF digital operators quickly embraced AMTOR and the race for HF digital innovation began. It continues to this day.

ARRL's HF Digital Handbook is not intended to be a sentimental retrospective, however. Instead, the book serves as a guide to understanding the most active HF digital modes in use today.

There is something within *ARRL's HF Digital Handbook* for every reader. Beginners will enjoy the practical advice and relaxed writing style. More advanced operators will appreciate the concise explanations of coding techniques and modulation methods, as well as the ample resource information.

With rapid advances in information technology, HF digital communication has become a moving target. New techniques are being developed on a regular basis as more powerful computers find their way into ham stations. *ARRL's HF Digital Handbook* is, therefore, a snapshot look at the current state of the art. The challenge to you will be to keep up to date with new modes and methods as they rapidly unfold!

David Sumner, K1ZZ

Executive Vice President
March 2004

Chapter ONE

Welcome to the World of HF Digital

Amateur Radio has entered the 21st Century. It is remarkable when you realize that in less than 100 years amateur communication has evolved from crude spark-gap technology to digital signal processing. Where hams once had to choose between voice and CW, we now enjoy a broad range of communication choices from television (slow and fast scan) to spread spectrum. Where we were once limited to frequencies below 1500 kHz, we now communicate on bands from medium waves to microwaves.

Amateur digital communication has also evolved. Look at the time line in **Figure 1-1**. From the end of World War II until the early '80s, radiotelegraphy, better known as *RTTY*, was the only HF digital mode available to amateurs. Then, in 1983, AMTOR made its debut, coinciding with the rising popularity of personal computers. It was the first amateur digital communication mode to offer error-free text transmission.

From the early '80s, the rate of change quickened to a fast gallop. Packet radio emerged by the middle '80s and, for a time, reigned as the most popular form of amateur digital communication.

Figure 1-1—The Amateur Radio digital time line.

As microprocessor technology became more sophisticated, we saw the rise of modes such as Clover, PACTOR and G-TOR that were capable of error-free exchanges under marginal band conditions (weak signals, interference and so on). In the late '90s there was an invention that harnessed personal computer technology to create a new digital mode for casual operating: PSK31. In the first years of the 21st Century, the evolution has continued with more HF digital modes such as MFSK16 and Q15X25.

Another powerful agent for change in the amateur digital community has been the Internet. With the possible exception of the personal computer, nothing else has had such a profound impact on the hobby. The Internet allowed amateurs to exchange information, including software, quickly and reliably. The development of the World Wide Web created a new kind of publishing arena where anyone could launch a personal Web site to promote his or her favorite aspects of Amateur Radio. As new ideas and applications flowed across the network, computers became essential components of modern ham stations. (By 2003, for example, more than 80% of all ARRL members used computers in their amateur stations, and more than 90% had Internet access.) The explosive growth of the Internet has had a substantial impact on amateur digital communication, HF and otherwise.

Let's take a brief look at current amateur HF digital communication modes and where they stand today.

RTTY

RTTY is the granddaddy of HF digital, although its popularity has been seriously undercut by PSK31 (more about that mode in a moment). However, RTTY is still the mode of choice for digital contesting and DXing.

AMTOR

Amateur Teleprinting Over Radio—AMTOR—enjoyed widespread popularity from about 1983 through 1991. Its distinctive *chirp-chirp* sound was a staple on the HF bands. Hams made ample use of its error-free text capability, even setting up automatic AMTOR mailbox operations (MBOs) where messages could be stored for later retrieval from anywhere in the world. AMTOR has since been superceded by faster, more versatile modes. It is rarely heard on the ham bands today.

PACKET

Although packet technology had been in existence since the early '70s, hams embraced it with gusto in the middle '80s. (Personal computers, again, were the driving force.) Packet is an error-detecting mode, which means that it is capable of communicating error-free information, including binary data (for images, software applications, etc). The problem with packet, as far as HF communication is concerned, is that it requires strong, "quiet" signals at both ends of the path to function efficiently. Packet doesn't tolerate signal fading, noise or interference, which makes it a poor choice for the chaotic world of HF.

Packet was much more successful on VHF and UHF. For nearly a decade packet flourished, primarily on the 2-meter band. Hams reveled in their newfound ability to send e-mail messages throughout the nation and the world, but the advent of affordable Internet access soon brought the party to a grinding halt. As the Internet skyrocketed to prominence, traditional packet declined just as rapidly. Bulletin board stations closed, networks collapsed and sales of packet equipment slowed to a trickle.

VHF packet retains a foothold today thanks to DX spotting networks (known as DX PacketClusters) and the moderate popularity of the Automatic Position Reporting System (APRS), a marriage of amateur packet radio and global positioning satellite technology. Despite its poor performance, HF packet remains stubbornly alive. Network 105, for example, is a group of HF packet users who operate on 14.105 MHz.

Popular HF Digital Frequencies	
Band (Meters)	Frequencies (MHz)
10	28.070—28.130
12	24.920—24.930
15	21.060—21.099
17	18.100—18.110
20	14.060—14.099[1]
30	10.120—10.150
40	7.060—7.099[2]
80	3.580—3.640

Notes

[1]This is the most active HF digital band

[2]Digital operators should avoid interfering with operators in ITU Regions 1 and 3, as well as Alaska, Hawaii and Puerto Rico, who may have phone privileges in this portion of 40 meters.

PACTOR

PACTOR strolled onto the telecommunications stage in 1991. It combined the best aspects of packet (the ability to pass binary data, for example) and the robust error-free nature of AMTOR. It was eagerly embraced by HF digital equipment manufacturers and became the number-one HF digital communication mode in a remarkably short period. PACTOR was popular for mailbox operations and other forms of message handling. As with packet, the Internet caused a serious decline in PACTOR activity, but it remains the most popular of the error-free modes.

PACTOR II debuted in the mid '90s as a rival to Clover, and the two have been doing battle for the hearts, minds and pocketbooks of HF communicators (commercial and amateur) ever since. Like Clover, PACTOR II uses DSP techniques and complex data coding to achieve extraordinary performance. Also, like Clover, the necessary equipment is quite expensive, which has slowed PACTOR II's acceptance in the ham community.

In 2002, PACTOR III appeared on the scene. It is even more robust, but its signal also occupies a substantial amount of spectrum.

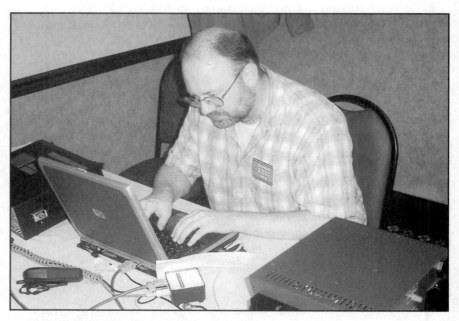

Dave Hassler, K7CCC, makes HF digital contacts at a digital special-event station.

CLOVER

Clover was unveiled in 1993 by the HAL Communications Corporation. It was one of the first HF digital modes to use sophisticated data coding, coupled with complex modulation schemes and digital processing technology, in an effort to overcome the vagaries of HF. Clover promised, and delivered, impressive performance even in the face of weak signals and terrible band conditions. This performance initially came at a stiff price—one that few hams could afford. As you'd expect, the high cost of Clover technology dampened enthusiasm in the beginning. Some hams adopted Clover, but it never became as popular as PACTOR and is still a rare mode on the amateur bands.

G-TOR

G-TOR was the brainchild of Kantronics, a digital communication equipment manufacturer. It was yet another high-performance mode, although not as costly as Clover or PACTOR II. Like both of the former, however, G-TOR was *proprietary*. That means that it is only available in equipment manufactured by Kantronics. Coming several years after the appearance of PACTOR, G-TOR never really captured the attention of HF digital operators.

PSK31

PSK31 could be viewed as a high-octane cousin of RTTY. It is not an error-free digital mode, but it offers excellent weak-signal performance. Peter Martinez, G3PLX, the same person who created AMTOR, invented PSK31. For a few years PSK31 languished in obscurity because special DSP hardware was necessary to use it. But in 1999, Peter designed a version of PSK31 that needed nothing more than a common computer soundcard. It was a simple piece of software that ran under *Windows* and used the soundcard as its interface to the transceiver. Peter made the software available at no cost on the Internet, and that was like tossing a lighted match into a can of gasoline. Within a few months, PSK31 exploded in the HF digital community and it is now the most popular mode for casual conversation. A higher-speed variant known as PSK63 appeared in 2003 and has gained some attention, particularly among contest operators.

Advanced software such as *MultiPSK* are capable of decoding several PSK31 signals simultaneously.

HELLSCHREIBER

Hellschreiber is not a new mode (it was pioneered in the 1920s and '30s by Rudolf Hell), but a number of hams are beginning to discover its possibilities. Unlike all of the other modes we've discussed so far, Hellschreiber is *visual*. That is to say, the signals "paint" the text on your screen much in the same sense that a television or fax signal paints an image.

One variation of Hellschreiber known as *Feld-Hell* works its magic by keying a CW transmitter ON for every black portion in a text character, and OFF for every white space. Timing is critical. Feld-Hell has drawn some interest among low power (QRP) operators because you can operate with simple (but stable) CW transmitters. Most Feld-Hell operation, however, is done using SSB transceivers using on/off tone "keying" to accomplish the same result. Feld-Hell is the most popular of the Hellschreiber modes.

You can also send text imagery by using different *frequencies* (tones) to represent the black and white areas. This version of Hellschreiber is called *Multi-Tone Hell*, or simply MT-Hell. There are several variations of MT-Hell in use.

MT-63

Pawel Jalocha, SP9VRC, invented MT-63. It is a keyboard-to-keyboard "live" mode operationally similar to RTTY and PSK31. With MT-63, however, the data components are spread over 64 different tones! This allows a tremendous amount of redundancy, assuring good reception even when as much as 25% of the data has been obliterated by noise, fading or interference. Thanks to its modulation structure, MT-63 offers excellent performance under poor conditions, even rivaling Clover and PACTOR II.

There is a certain amount of controversy surrounding MT-63 in the amateur community. Its signal can be quite wide (2 kHz). With crowded conditions in the HF digital subbands today, the movement has been toward narrow signals. PSK31, for example, is only about 31 Hz wide.

MFSK16

This mode was brought to the forefront through an article by Murray Greenman, ZL1BPU, which appeared in the January 2001 issue of *QST*. MFSK16 uses several different tones to communicate in difficult conditions, yet remaining within a bandwidth of about 300 Hz. The mode was developed as a joint effort between ZL1BPU and Nino Porcino, IZ8BLY. Nino's *Stream* software introduced MFSK16 to the ham community at large.

THROB

Lionel Sear, G3PPT, developed Throb. Throb is another multi-frequency shift-keyed mode like MFSK16. Unlike MFSK16, which transmits one of 16 audio tones in succession at a 15.625 baud rate, Throb sends two out of a possible nine tones simultaneously at a user-selectable rate of 1, 2 or 4 baud (10, 20 or 40 WPM) and a bandwidth of 72 Hz (144 Hz at 40 WPM). Thanks to its soft keying waveform, Throb has a distinctive throbbing sound.

A sound card "waterfall" display showing the profile of a typical Q15X25 signal.

Q15X25

Q15X25 is a DSP intensive mode that operates like a packet modem to provide an error-free mode that is much faster and more reliable on HF than packet. As this edition went to press, only a few operators were experimenting with Q15X25, but the results were promising.

DOMINO

Domino is a conversational HF digital mode that debuted in early 2004. Similar in some respects to MFSK16, domino is generating interest for its ability to provide readable copy over less-than-stable propagation paths, particularly on the low bands. When this book was written, domino software was only available for the *Windows* operating system.

Chapter TWO

Assembling Your HF Digital Station

In the old days of HF digital, back when RTTY was your only option, setting up a station wasn't a trivial exercise. You had to make room for a bulky mechanical teletype machine, cobble together an interface to your radio to actuate the teletype, and install an oscilloscope to help you tune the signal. You sent text by typing on the teletype's awkward "green keys," and read the other station's replies on rolls of yellow paper.

Thanks to personal computers and microprocessor technology it is infinitely easier to assemble an HF digital station these days. The only hurdle is to bridge the gap between the digital world of your computer and the analog world of your transceiver.

DIGITAL TO ANALOG—AND BACK AGAIN

Data exists in your computer in the form of changing voltages. Five volts might represent a binary "1" while zero volts may represent a binary "0." But a radio can't transmit changing voltages—at least not without a little translation help.

In the case of digital communication, our translator is a modulator/demodulator, otherwise known as a *modem*. A modem takes the binary data from your computer and translates it into modulated audio that can be sent over a radio. This audio consists of tones that change their frequencies, phase, amplitude and so on.

RTTY, for example, communicates 1s and 0s by creating a signal that shifts rapidly between two frequencies. When the shifting signal is an audio tone applied to a transceiver, the technique is known as audio frequency shift keying, or *AFSK*. You'll often see transceiver manuals referring to this as frequency shift keying, or *FSK*, and this can be a little confusing. True FSK involves changing the frequency of your rig's master oscillator from one *RF* frequency to another in sync with the raw data from your computer (the data isn't translated into an audio frequency signal). Few RTTY operators use FSK these days, although there may be some advantages in doing so (see the "Filtering" sidebar). Most hams prefer AFSK because it will work with any SSB transceiver. With either method, the result on the receiving end is the same (see **Figure 2-1**).

Filtering

Most communications processors and sound card programs implement some form of audio filtering to reduce the signal chaos and make it easier to decode the data you want. Even so, such filtering is occasionally insufficient, particularly when the bands are very crowded (during contests, for example).

If your transceiver has a built-in audio filter—many modern rigs feature digital signal processing (DSP) filters—you can use it to dramatically reduce interference and improve your data throughput. You can also purchase an external audio filter to achieve the same result.

Filtering in the intermediate frequency (IF) stages of your radio is probably most effective at keeping adjacent frequency interference at bay. HF digital operators typically use 500-Hz IF filters for RTTY, especially when contesting and DX hunting. You can use narrow IF filters for PSK31, MFSK16, but these modes generally employ "panoramic" software that scans the entire receive audio bandwidth (typically 100 to 3000 Hz). By switching in a 500-Hz IF filter, you will severely restrict the audio bandwidth. Other modes are too wide for use with narrow filters (PACTOR II, III and MT-63, just to name a few).

Check the IF filter descriptions carefully and read the fine print. There is a "gotcha" waiting for the unwary! Many transceivers are designed to allow you to select these narrow IF filters *only* when you have the radio in the "RTTY" (sometimes referred to as "data" or "FSK") or CW modes. That's fine if you are operating PACTOR, AMTOR or RTTY, but other modes such as PSK31, Clover and PACTOR II require the radio to operate in SSB. Many transceivers will *not* allow you to choose narrow IF filtering when you select SSB.

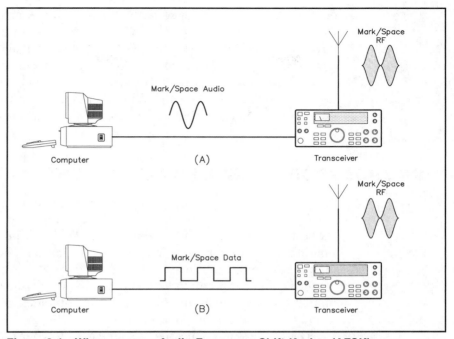

Figure 2-1—When you use Audio Frequency Shift Keying (AFSK), your computer sound card or multimode processor generates audio tones, which you feed to your transceiver to create RF (A). With Frequency Shift Keying (FSK), however, your computer or processor only generates data pulses (B). When fed to an FSK-capable transceiver, these data pulses signal the radio to transmit the Mark or Space signals. Whether you're operating FSK or AFSK, the results are essentially the same. The advantage of FSK is that many radios only implement narrow IF receive filtering when in the FSK mode. This is a big plus for DXers or contesters. On the other hand, FSK is strictly a binary ON/OFF system. HF digital modes such as PSK31, CLOVER, MFSK16 and Hellschreiber cannot run under conventional FSK. You must operate these modes in AFSK.

MFSK16 also uses a frequency-shifting scheme, but it spreads the information over 16 different signals. The idea is safety in numbers—if one signal is obliterated by interference, another signal might get through. Several other HF digital systems use variations of this multi-frequency technique.

PSK31 and PSK63, on the other hand, communicate binary data by shifting the phase of a single audio frequency, which is then applied to the transceiver. This is known as *phase shift keying*. The phase shifts correspond to binary 1s and 0s.

But what about reception? The modem waiting patiently at the other end of the path is equipped with signal decoders and sharp audio filters—electronic or digital. It will only respond to signals *if* they have the proper characteristics. Off-frequency signals are ignored, and signals separated by incorrect shifts or using incorrect modulation never make it past the filters. But when the tones hit the targets, the modem instantly converts them into data pulses—which soon wind up in your computer. Your computer software takes it from there.

SOUNDCARDS AS HF DIGITAL MODEMS

You may already be the proud owner of an HF digital modem—your PC sound card. Sound cards do exactly what modems do: convert data to audio and audio to data. With the proper software running in the background, your PC can become a high-performance digital communication machine.

Just about every computer manufactured within the last five years includes sound capability. Even if your computer doesn't have a sound card, you can add one for as little as $30.

The concept of connecting a sound card to your radio is simple. Sound comes out of your radio and goes into your computer to be

---

Transceiver Accessory Jacks

The nice thing about modern transceivers is that most are equipped with handy rear panel accessory (or auxiliary) jacks. These multipin jacks usually feature a transmit/receive keying line, a fixed-level receive-audio output and a transmit audio input. Accessory jack connections make it astonishingly easy to set up your HF digital station.

The fixed-level receive-audio output is exactly what your sound card or processor needs to function efficiently. Because it is a fixed, continuous audio source, you can turn down the audio gain on your transceiver—thereby preserving the peace in your household—without affecting the receive performance.

A keying line at the accessory jack means that your sound card interface or processor can automatically switch your radio from transit to receive as necessary.

And a transmit audio input is tailor-made for HF digital signals. Unlike your microphone jack, it expects the higher audio levels generated by your soundcard or modem.

processed, or decoded, in the receive path. Processed sound comes out of your computer and goes into your radio to be modulated and transmitted. The input to the sound card is the receive (audio) signal and the output is the transmitted (audio) signal. Most of the work is done (inside the computer) with the incredible software available to us.

Sound cards come in lots of flavors: 8 bit, 16 bit, 32 bit, wave table synthesis, ISA, PCI, gold, 128, "surround sound" and so on. I refer to a sound "card," but a computer can, instead, use sound processing chips on the motherboard. That is usually the case with laptops. There are some new external sound adapters that function as a sound card but are connected externally through a USB port. If your computer has sound it will have at least a headphone, microphone or speaker jack. If so, you can use it with your radio to communicate. A complex sound card is not needed—a modern, though inexpensive PCI sound card will work very well and a simple one will be easier to connect and operate. Older, ISA bus cards will work with most Amateur Radio programs but might have limited dynamic range and slower processing.

Even the simplest of sound cards can be complicated. They can have as few as two external connections but there may be as many as twelve or more. At the rear of your computer you may find LINE IN, MIC IN, LINE OUT, SPEAKER OUT, PCM OUT, PCM IN, JOYSTICK, FIREWIRE, S/PDIF, REAR CHANNELS or SURROUND jacks, just to name a few. Connections appear not only on the outside, but inside, as well. The main internal connection is to the ISA or PCI bus and this is by edge connection to the board. There may also be CD audio, telephone, daughterboard and PC speaker connections inside and on the board, as well.

The first thing to do is to identify which connection is which, at least at the card edge bracket, outside the board. The jacks are usually poorly marked with nonstandard international symbols or color codes.

Depending on your computer, you may be able to choose your receive audio connection from either MIC INPUT or LINE INPUT. Anything else you find is not an audio input. If you do have a choice, use the LINE INPUT for the receive audio from your radio. Although the MIC INPUT jack can be used, it will have much more gain than you need and you may find adjustment quite critical. The MIC INPUT jack will work better, however, if your sound card has an "advanced" option to select a 20 dB attenuator. You should not need ground isolation for receive audio as it is at a high level and is normally not susceptible to ground loops. You may also be able to choose from several outputs that appear on the radio. Your radio may have SPEAKER, HEADPHONE, LINE OUT, RECORD, PHONE PATCH and

This SoundBlaster sound card by Creative Labs features several input and output ports.

DATA OUTPUT jacks available (see the sidebar "Transceiver Accessory Jacks"). These may be fixed output or variable output (using the radio's volume control). Be careful with radio's DATA OUTPUT jack—it may not work on all modes.

For the transmit connection, you will have a choice of the computer's HEADPHONE OUTPUT, LINE OUTPUT, SPEAKER OUTPUT or a combination of these. The SPEAKER OUTPUT is usually the best choice as it will drive almost anything you hook to it. The SPEAKER OUTPUT has a very low source impedance making it less susceptible to load current and RF. Any one of these outputs will usually work fine, provided you do not load down a line or headphone output by using very low impedance speakers or headphones to monitor computer-transmitted audio. The transmit audio connection must have full ground isolation through your interface, especially if it drives the MIC INPUT of the radio. This usually means a line-coupling transformer of 1:1 ratio and 600Ω impedance. RadioShack part no. 273-1374 will work.

Again, DATA INPUT jacks may not work the way you expect. Never use the digital input or output of your sound card. Even though you may wish to operate a digital mode, it will not work. You must use an analog audio connection, not a digital one. These jacks may be labeled PCM AUDIO and they have a digital data stream coming out of them, but it's not audio. Currently manufactured radios require analog audio.

Setting Levels

Setting the sound card levels correctly is an area in which you may run into difficulty. Sound cards are much more complex than you might think; most sound cards have more than 35 separate adjustments supported by two major virtual control panels. No two computers are alike, and there are always several different ways to get the same results. To make matters worse, once you adjust your sound card don't expect it to stay adjusted. Running other programs and rebooting your computer may reset your sound card parameters.

You may find that you have to readjust your card the next time you need to use it for communications. Sound card control is accessed through several virtual control panels. The sound card may also be controlled automatically through the software programs that you use. There can be many analog and digital signal paths in a typical sound card. Your job is to identify which ones you are connected to and make those connections work. When you single-click (left) the speaker icon in the bottom right corner of your computer screen you get one simple up/down slider with a mute switch. If you double-click that same icon, however, you get a large control panel for playback as shown in **Figure 2-2**.

Your control panel may be different. Instead of saying "Volume Control" at the top left corner, it may say "Playback" or it may have "Select" instead of "Mute" boxes at the bottom. Each section has a label indicating the control for a single mono or stereo signal path: Volume Control, Wave, MIDI, CD Player, etc. The word Balance that appears to be part of a section label is not; it is just a label for the left/right slider directly beneath it. This is the playback, output or monitor control panel or, as hams would call it, the transmit control panel. This panel's only function is to adjust what comes out of your sound card. The only exception would be if you had an older sound card—the controls might be ganged with the recording control panels; they then could not be adjusted independently. **Figure 2-3** shows a typical "Recording" control panel. This panel is carefully hidden in *Windows* and I bet you didn't know it was there unless

Figure 2-2—When you single-click (left) the speaker icon in the bottom right corner of your computer screen you get one simple up/down slider with a mute switch. If you double-click that same icon, however, you get a large control panel for playback.

Figure 2-3—A typical sound card recording control panel. This panel controls the sounds going to your sound card software from your radio.

you are already operating the sound card modes. I don't know why the folks who wrote *Windows* hid it so well but here's how to find it: double click the speaker icon, then "Options," "Properties," "Recording" and finally, "OK." Surprise…another control panel appears! The "Recording Control" panel is used to turn on and adjust the input signals from both analog (audio) and digital inputs and to feed those input signals to the software for processing. This functions as a receive control panel. It does not normally control transmit unless you are transmitting an audio signal that is being fed from your radio, through your computer and software, and processed in real time.

An example would be microphone equalization or speech processing. Depending on your sound card there may be buttons for "Advanced" settings. Here you can find advanced settings for tone control, microphone gain, recording monitoring, etc. Be careful with the recording monitor settings as they can cause an internal or external feedback loop.

As you look at these controls, note that the sliders are up, the balance is centered; and the inputs and outputs are unmuted. You can be assured that something *won't* work if you have any one of these sliders all the way down or that input muted. Again, your sound card may be different, but if it says "Select" instead of "Mute" you have to check the box instead of unchecking it.

SOUND CARD INTERFACES

Configuring your sound card levels is one thing, but getting the audio to and from your radio is another. You also need to provide a way for your computer to switch your transceiver between receive and transmit. This is where the *sound card interface* comes into play.

Most amateurs use commercial sound card interfaces such as those made by MFJ Enterprises, West Mountain Radio and Tigertronics (see the Resources section of this book for contact information). These handy boxes take care of everything. They match the audio levels, isolate the audio lines and provide transmit/receive switching, usually with your computer's serial (COM) port.

You can also make your own interface by simply isolating the audio lines and cobbling together a single-transistor switch to connect to your COM port. See **Figure 2-4**.

Figure 2-5 shows a typical interface connection between a computer and a transceiver. Note that the transmit audio connects to the radio through the interface. By doing so, the interface can provide isolation. Some interfaces also include a transmit audio adjustment, although this can also be accomplished at the computer, as we've already discussed.

Look closely at Figure 2-5 and you'll see that the receive audio cable is connected directly between the radio and the sound card input. Many interfaces use this approach, but others also pass the receive audio through the interface and provide isolation for this signal path as well.

It's important to mention that you may also be able to use the VOX (voice-operated switching) function on your transceiver to automatically switch from transmit to receive when it senses the transmit audio from

Figure 2-4—This simple circuit will allow your computer's COM port to key your transceiver when you're using sound card software. You can choose to connect to either the RTS or DTR pins at the COM port. Some software packages key the transceiver by sending a logic "high" to one pin or the other. RadioShack part numbers are shown in parentheses.
D1, D2—1N4001 diodes (276-1101)
R1—2.2 kΩ resistor, ¼ W (271-1325)
Q1—MPS-2222A transistor (276-2009)

Figure 2-5— A typical interface connection between a computer and a transceiver. Note that the transmit audio connects to the radio through the interface. By doing so, the interface can provide isolation.

your sound card. This approach completely removes the need for a T/R switching circuit, COM port and so on. The Tigertronics SignaLink interface uses this technique by incorporating its own VOX circuit, freeing the computer COM port for other uses.

The weakness of this technique is that it will cause your radio to

One of the RIGblaster sound card interfaces manufactured by West Mountain Radio.

transmit when it senses *any* audio from your computer—including miscellaneous beeps, music, etc.

MULTIMODE PROCESSORS

Until sound card software appeared on the market, the most common HF digital interface was the *multimode processor*, or what some refer to as a *multimode TNC*. This device offers several HF digital communication modes in a single unit that usually sits alongside your radio. The exception is the HAL Communications P38 that comes in the form of a circuit "card" that fits *inside* your PC.

Multimode processors offer several HF digital modes, plus a cornucopia of features such as message mailboxes, remote control and much more. The processors are relatively easy to hook up between your computer and your transceiver (see **Figure 2-6**). The computer uses terminal software to "talk" to the processor. The processor manufacturer usually provides this software, but there are third-party sources as well. Between the processor and the radio you need to run cables for receive audio, transmit/receive switching and transmit audio.

But with so many sound card-based modes available, what are the advantages of purchasing an outboard processor?

• You can use almost *any* computer with a multimode processor. The processor merely asks the computer to send and receive information. This is a easy task for even the oldest machines. As long as the computer has

If you want to try Clover as well as RTTY and PACTOR I, the solutions are HAL Communications P38 or P38DX. The P38 plugs into your PC buss slot while the P38DX is an outboard unit. Both products sell at less than $400.

terminal software that can communicate with the processor—or if the computer can run the terminal software provided by the manufacturer—you're in business. You could use an "ancient" 286 or 386 PC, a used $200 laptop or whatever.

• Many multimode processors offer features that are not presently available with soundcard-based software. Mailboxes and automatic, stand-alone operations come to mind. Your processor can be set up to receive and process messages without the need for supervision by your

Figure 2-6—A multimode communication processor connects to the COM port of your computer and to your transceiver. Use short, shielded cables for all connections.

The SCS PTC-IIe is the only multimode communication processor that offers PACTOR II. The original PTC-II was priced at nearly $1000, which made it slow to catch on in the ham community. The PTC-IIe, however, sells for less than $700.

computer. You can ignore the processor completely and use your PC to do other work.

• Clover, G-TOR, PACTOR II and PACTOR III are available *only* with multimode processors. If you wish to try these modes, you must purchase a HAL Communications unit (for Clover), a Kantronics KAM (for G-TOR) or an SCS PTC-IIe (for PACTOR II and III). All of these products will also operate RTTY, PACTOR I, AMTOR and, in the case of the SCS PTC-IIe, PSK31.

Multimode communication processors include the Kantronics KAM Plus, the Timewave PK-232/DSP and the MFJ-1278B.

THE HF DIGITAL TRANSCEIVER

Just about any modern SSB transceiver will do double duty as your HF digital radio. However, if you plan to dabble in the handshaking modes such as AMTOR, PACTOR I, PACTOR II, PACTOR III, Clover or G-TOR you want a radio that can jump from transmit to receive (and back again) very quickly—usually in less than 30 milliseconds. When a link is established and your computer sends a chunk of data, you must be ready to receive data from the receiving station right away. In other words, your radio has to exit the transmit mode and be ready to receive by the time the data signal comes screaming back at the speed of light. Fortunately, most radios manufactured after 1985 can perform this trick reasonably well. When in doubt, however, check the transceiver specifications carefully.

For the other HF digital modes, any SSB radio, modern or otherwise, is sufficient as long as it is reasonably stable. You're not engaging in the handshake dance. This means that you don't have to be too concerned about how fast your rig jumps from transmit to receive.

The only remaining concern is output power. When you transmit with modes that demand long transmit intervals, you're asking your rig to produce full output for several minutes at a time—maybe longer if you're a slow typist. This is known as a *100% duty cycle*. Most transceivers won't tolerate this kind of punishment; they're designed for the lower duty cycles of SSB or CW. So, unless you are running a burst mode such as PACTOR (all flavors) Clover or G-TOR, it pays to reduce your output. Some manufacturers recommend a 50% reduction.

Chapter THREE

RTTY

As we discussed in Chapter 1, RTTY is the "old man" of the HF digital modes. Despite more than five decades of amateur use it remains a popular choice. There are several reasons for this:

(1) RTTY hardware is easy to set up. All it takes is one of the multimode controllers described in Chapter 2, or a PC equipped with a soundcard. You can transmit RTTY with *any* SSB transceiver—new or old.

(2) RTTY is easy to operate. Because RTTY is not a "handshaking" mode, you do not set up a link with elaborately timed protocols. Enjoying a RTTY conversation is a matter of just typing and transmitting. RTTY lends itself well to contests and DX pileups where 100% error-free text is not required.

As with most HF digital modes, the majority of the activity is on 20 meters (see the frequency list in Chapter 1). You'll also hear RTTY occasionally on 40 and 15 meters. Of course, during contests you'll hear RTTY on almost every band!

MARK AND SPACE

Each character in the Baudot RTTY code is composed of five bits (see the sidebar, "The Baudot Code"). In amateur RTTY communication a "1" bit is usually represented by a 2125-Hz tone and is known as a *mark*. A "0" bit is represented by a 2295-Hz tone called a *space*. There is also a start pulse at the beginning of the bit string and a stop pulse at the end (see **Figure 3-1**). The data is commonly sent at a rate of 60 WPM, or 45 baud.

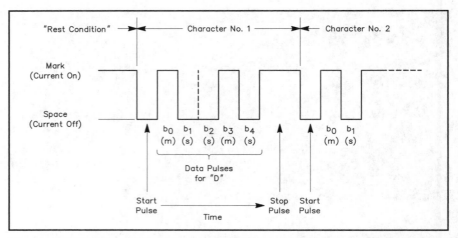

Figure 3-1-~~This~~ is a diagram of a RTTY signal as the letter 'D" is being sent. A start pulse begins the character, followed by the five bits (b0-b4) that define it. A stop pulse signals the end of the character.

Shift

Grab your calculator and do a bit of subtraction:
2295 Hz – 2125 Hz = 170 Hz

In the answer shown above, 170 Hz is the difference or *shift* between the mark and space frequencies. The Amateur Radio RTTY standard is to use either a 170- or 200-Hz shift. Multimode communications processors often use a 200-Hz shift with the mark tone at 2110 Hz and the space tone at 2310 Hz. RTTY soundcard software and transceivers running in the FSK mode tend to default to the 170-Hz shift. Fortunately, both shifts share the same center frequency (2210 Hz), which makes them *generally* compatible. This means that you don't usually need to worry whether the station you are attempting to contact is using a 170- or 200-Hz shift. In some weak-signal conditions, however, you may find that you need to tune carefully so that your shift "straddles" that of the other stations.

TUNING AND DECODING THE RTTY SIGNAL

Every RTTY decoder, whether it works in software or hardware, incorporates a set of mark and space audio filters. You can think of these filters as dual windows that only open for tones that are at the correct mark and space frequencies, and separated by the proper shift. The mark and space filtering circuitry detects and decodes the tones into digital 1s and 0s, which is exactly what your computer or processor needs to provide text on your screen. The more sensitive and selective your mark/space detectors, the better your RTTY performance, especially as it involves your ability to copy weak signals through interference.

It's easy to understand why tuning a RTTY signal (and just about any other data signal) is so critical—and why a good tuning indicator is one of your best HF digital tools. Whenever you stumble upon a RTTY signal, you must quickly tune your receiver until its mark and space tones fall within the "skirts" of the filters and are detected. It's possible to do this by ear once you become accustomed to the sound of a properly tuned RTTY transmission, but few of us have the necessary patience. Instead, we rely on visual indicators to guide us.

The old method of tuning was to use an oscilloscope. You tweaked the signal until two ellipses representing the mark and space tones crossed in the middle of the screen. This was known as the *crossed bananas* display (see **Figure 3-2**). Some modern software and hardware tuning indicators pay homage to the crossed bananas by providing a display in the shape of a plus (+) sign, or cross. In hardware such as the HAL Communications DXP38 multimode processor, for example, you tune until the + display

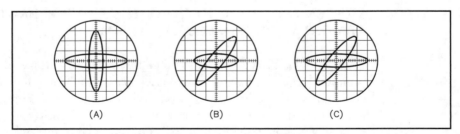

(A)   (B)   (C)

Figure 3-2—This is the classic crossed bananas RTTY tuning display. Pattern A indicates that the signal has been tuned corrected. At B the receiver is slightly off frequency, while C indicates that the transmitting station is using a shift that differs from your processor or modem setting. Although hardly any RTTY operators use oscilloscope tuning today, modern tuning indicators still rely on the same principle. Some even attempt to emulate the crossed bananas display.

flashes in sync with the RTTY signal. The Kantronics, MFJ and Timewave processors use a "bouncing" LED bargraph, but the idea is fundamentally the same.

CONVERSING WITH RTTY

As with so many aspects of Amateur Radio, I highly recommend that you begin by listening. Tune between 14.080 and 14.099 MHz and listen for the long, continuous *blee-blee-blee-blee* signals of RTTY. (If you hear chirping, it isn't RTTY!)

Make sure your transceiver is set for lower sideband (LSB). That is the RTTY convention. The exception is when you are operating your rig in the "FSK" mode (sometimes labeled "DATA" or "RTTY"). As we discussed in Chapter 2, many hams prefer operating this way because it allows them to use narrow IF filters to reduce interference. When you operate in FSK, your modem, soundcard or processor is *not* generating the mark and space tones. They're merely sending data pulses to the radio and the radio is creating its own mark and space signals. (This often requires a special connection to the transceiver. Consult your manual.)

As you tune the RTTY signal, watch your tuning indicator. Tune slowly until you see that the mark and space tones are being decoded. At this point you should see letters marching across your screen. Notice how the conversation flows just like a voice or CW ragchew.

KF6I DE WB8IMY . . . YES, I HEARD FROM SAM JUST YESTERDAY. HE SAID THAT HIS TOWER PROJECT WAS ALMOST FINISHED. KF6I DE WB8IMY K

If you want to call CQ, the procedure is simple. Some programs have "canned" CQ messages (known as *macros*) that you can customize with your call sign. Others allow you to type off the air, filling a buffer with your CQ and storing it temporarily until you're ready to go.

Let's assume that you have a CQ stored in your buffer right now. Press the key that puts your rig in the transmit mode. Now tap the key that spills the contents of your buffer into the modem. If you're monitoring your own signal you'll hear the delightful chatter of RTTY and see something like this on your screen:

CQ CQ CQ CQ CQ CQ WB8IMY WB8IMY WB8IMY
CQ CQ CQ CQ CQ CQ WB8IMY WB8IMY WB8IMY K K

Now jump back to receive. That's all there is to it!

Notice how my CQ is short and to the point. Did you also notice that I repeated everything several times? *Remember that RTTY lacks error detection.* If you want to make certain that the other station copied what you sent, it helps to repeat it. You'll see this often in contest exchanges. For example:

N6ATQ DE N1RL . . . UR 549 549. STATE IS CT CT. DE N1RL K

On the other hand, if you know that the other station is copying you well, there is no need to repeat information.

You'll notice that many RTTY programs have three text transmission options: Character out, Word out, Line out. If you are a RTTY purist, who once used the "green keys" on an old Teletype Model 28 teletypewriter, then you can select Character out and every letter will be typed as soon as you send it. However, for those more used to modern computers, Word out means that even if the computer has caught up with your typing, it will not send the last word until you have typed a space after that word. This gives you a chance to correct the spelling in the word, using the backspace key, without sending the wrong characters. Line out means that you must reach the end of a line or type a carriage return to send the characters. ine out is probably not suitable for most operators. It means that your transmitter simply sends either a constant tone or a "diddle" while waiting for your line to be complete, and then you must wait for the last line to be transmitted before you can receive.

Another option to investigate in your RTTY software is Unshift On Space (UOS). There is a benefit to using UOS when receiving. Two

The software tuning indicator provided by *WriteLog*, a RTTY contest software package (see Chapter 11).

special characters, LTRS and FIGS, are used by the RTTY code to indicate to the computer or processor whether the characters that follow will letters or figures (numbers and punctuation). If you enable UOS, your software will exit the FIGS shift as soon as there is a space, so your display does not print out garbage if the software misses the LTRS shift character because of noise or interference.

THE MYSTERY SIGNAL

What happens if you stumble across a RTTY signal that you cannot copy? The signal is strong enough, and you seem to be doing all the right things, but you see gibberish on your screen or nothing at all. Why?

It looks like you need to do a little detective work. Check the following:

• Is the signal "upside down"? The RF frequency of the mark signal is usually higher than the RF frequency of the space signal, but there is no law that dictates this standard. With most processors and software you can flip the relationship with the push of a button or the click of a mouse.

There are many ways to call CQ on RTTY. Here is a CQ copied from WA5TLP using *MMTTY* software on 20 meters. The number/character gibberish is caused by noise between transmissions.

• Is the station running in upper sideband (USB) rather than lower sideband (LSB)?

• Are the operators really using signals that have 170- or 200-Hz shifts at 45 baud? Some RTTY operators might choose to run at 75 baud when sending lengthy text. Others may choose to use oddball shifts.

CHASING RTTY DX

RTTY is still the most widely used mode for HF digital DXing. You can work 100 countries to earn your RTTY DX Century Club (DXCC) award, and even climb the ladder to the stratospheric heights of RTTY DXCC Honor Roll. RTTY DXing is competitive and highly rewarding.

Like any other form of DXing, the quest for RTTY DX demands patience and skill. When a DXpedition is on the air with RTTY from a rare DXCC entity, your signal will be in competition with thousands of other HF digital operators who want to work the station as badly as you! Sometimes pure luck is the winning factor, but there are several tricks of the trade that you can use to tweak the odds in your favor.

Don't Call...Yet

Let's say that you're tuning through the HF digital subbands one day and you stumble across a screaming mass of RTTY signals. On your computer screen you see that everyone seems to be frantically calling a DX station. Oh, boy! It's a pileup!

You can't actually hear the DX station that has everyone so excited, but what the heck, you'll activate your transceiver and throw your call sign into the fray, right? *Wrong!*

Never transmit even a microwatt of RF until you can copy the DX station. Tossing your call sign in blindly is pointless and will only add to the pandemonium. Instead, take a deep breath and wait. When the calls subside, can you see text from the DX station on your screen? If not, the station is probably too weak for you to work (don't even bother), or he may be working "split." More about that in a moment.

If you can copy the DX station, watch the exchange carefully. Is he calling for certain stations only? In other words, is he sending instructions such as "North America only"? Calling in direct violation of the DX station's instructions is a good way to get yourself blacklisted in his log. (No QSL card for you—ever!) Does he just want signal reports, or is he in the mood for brief chats? Most DX stations simply want "599" and possibly your location—period. Don't give them more than they are asking for. (A DX RTTY station on a rare island doesn't care what kind weather you are experiencing at the moment.)

Working the Split

When DX RTTY pileups threaten to spin out of control, many DX operators will resort to working "split." In this case, "split" means split frequency. The DX station will transmit on one frequency while listening for calls on another frequency (or range of frequencies).

A good DX operator will announce the fact that he is working split with almost every exchange. That's why it is so important to listen to a pileup before you throw yourself into the middle. If you tune into a pileup and cannot hear the DX station, tune below the pileup and see if you copy the DX station there. If his signal is strong enough, he shouldn't be hard to find if he is working split. His signal will seem to be by itself, answering calls that you cannot hear. This is a major clue that a split operation is taking place. Watch for copy such as...

CQ DX DE FOØAAA, UP 10 (He is listening up 10 kHz)
CQ DX DE FOØAAA, 14085-14090 (He is listening between 14085 and 14090 kHz)

Whatever you do, *never call a split DX operation on the station's transmitting frequency*. Your screen will quickly fill with rude comments from others who are listening. Instead, put your transceiver into the split-frequency mode (better drag out your rig manual!). Set your radio to receive on the DX station's transmitting frequency and transmit on his listening frequency. If the DX station is listening through a range of frequencies, you'll need to select a spot where you think you'll be heard. Change your transmit frequency if this particular "fishing spot" doesn't seem to be working.

Short and Sweet

When you've done your listening homework and you're ready for battle, by all means fire at will. Wait until the DX station finishes an exchange. He'll signal that he is ready for another call by sending "QRZ?" or something similar. When it's time to transmit, make it short and to the point, like this...

WB8IMY WB8IMY WB8IMY K

Listen again. Has he responded to anyone yet? If the answer is "no" and other stations are still calling, the DX is probably trying to sort out the alphabet soup of confusion on his screen. Fire again!

WB8IMY WB8IMY WB8IMY KK

You might make it through at just the right moment when other signals subside briefly, or when the ionosphere gives you an unexpected boost. But if no one is calling, or if you hear the DX station calling someone else, *stop*. You lost this round, so give the lucky winner his chance to be heard. Your next opportunity will be coming up shortly.

Did He Call You?

Watch your screen carefully. If the DX station only copied a fragment of your call sign, he might send something like...

IMY IMY AGAIN??

In this instance he copied only the last three letters of my call sign ("IMY"). Fading and flutter can make RTTY signals difficult to copy clearly. See **Figure 3-3**. The best thing to do is reply right away, sending your call sign three times just like before.

```
MND WAS CEIVINGK RTTY FOR A LITTLE OVER A YEAR BUT
ONLY BEGAN TRANSMITTING ABOUTV 3 OR 4 WEEKS AGO.  USING MMTTYHERE RUMING 4 ;2-55s FROM ATHROTTLE

D BACK IC
746 TO A CAROLIN WINDOM AT ABOU 18 FEET.  FINE O
 THE WEATF  WELL, ILJD TRADSOUO
RITT NOW.  ;23;3 h-$-?975 - FOT OR A LITTLE BETTER OF EBOW ON THE GROUND FRO FO
 TWO MONTHS NOW
.  WINDTER CAME EARLY THIS YEAR TO MAKE UP FOR LAST!  TEMP ABOU_
```

Figure 3-3—Here is an actual on-air example of how fading can distort a RTTY DX signal. Notice the missing or incorrect letters. This example represents about 50-60% copy, which is probably sufficient to at least make a brief DX contact.

The Baudot Code

By Bill Henry, K9GWT

One of the first codes used with mechanical printing machines used a total of five data pulses to represent the alphabet, numerals and symbols. This code is commonly called the Baudot or Murray telegraph code after the work done by these two pioneers. Although commonly called the Baudot code in the United States, a similar code is usually called the Murray code in other parts of the world and is formally defined as the International Telegraphic No. 2 Baudot Code in part 97.69 of the FCC Rules. This standard defines the codes for letters, numbers and the slant or fraction bar but allows variations in the choice of code combinations for punctuation. US amateurs have generally adopted a version of the so-called "Military Standard" code arrangement for punctuation, due largely to the ready availability of military surplus machines in the post-1945 years. Amateurs in other countries (particularly in Europe) have standardized on the CCITT No. 2 code arrangement that is similar to the U.S. standard, but has minor symbol and code arrangement differences.

Since each of the five data pulses can be in either a mark or space condition (two possible states per pulses), a total of $2 \times 2 \times 2 \times 2 \times 2 = 2$ to the fifth = 32 different codes combinations are possible. Since it is necessary to provide transmissions of all 26 letters, 10 numerals plus punctuation, the 32 code combinations are not sufficient. Using the code twice solves this problem: once in the Letters (LTRS) case and again in the Figures (FIGS) case. Two special characters, LTRS and FIGS, are used to indicate to the computer or processor whether the following characters will be of the letters or figures case.

The Baudot code has seen extensive commercial use throughout the world and is still actively utilized for international wire communications, press and weather. Due to the ready availability of Baudot mechanical equipment, this code will continue to be quite popular among radio amateurs. However, the lack of code space for control, extended punctuation, or lower case letters is a severe limitation of the 5-unit Baudot code. These limitations are particularly inconvenient in computer applications.

Table 3-1 depicts the Baudot Code Set (ITA#2). The leftmost bit is the Most Significant Bit (MSB), transmitted last. The rightmost bit is the Least Significant Bit (LSB), transmitted first. The associated letters and figures (case) characters are also listed, along with the hexadecimal representation of the characters.

Table 3-1
The Baudot Code

Bits	LTRS	FIGS	HEX
00011	A	-	03
11001	B	?	19
01110	C	:	0E
01001	D	$	09
00001	E	3	01
01101	F	!	0D
11010	G	&	1A
10100	H	STOP	14
00110	I	8	06
01011	J	'	0B
01111	K	(	0F
10010	L	)	12
11100	M	.	1C
01100	N	,	0C
11000	O	9	18
10110	P	0	16
10111	Q	1	17
01010	R	4	0A
00101	S	BELL	05
10000	T	5	10
00111	U	7	07
11110	V	;	1E
10011	W	2	13
11101	X	/	1D
10101	Y	6	15
10001	Z	"	11
00000	n/a	n/a	00
01000	CR	CR	08
00010	LF	LF	02
00100	SP	SP	04
11111	LTRS	LTRS	1F
11011	FIGS	FIGS	1B

If luck is on your side, you'll see…

WB8IMY DE FOØAAA . . . TNX. 599. QSL? KK

And with excited fingers you answer…

QSL. UR 599. TNX AND 73 DE WB8IMY K

TRACKING THE DX

The most direct method for tracking RTTY DX is to tune through the bands and see who is on the air. With practice you'll learn when particular areas of the world are open to you. For example, 10 meters tends to open from the early afternoon into early evening while 40 meters is only open for DX at night. Twenty meters can provide DX at almost any time, which is why it is the most popular RTTY band.

Another method is to check the online DX WebClusters (see **Figure 3-4**). These sites collect DX information from operators throughout the world. Don't depend too heavily on these sites, though. Many DX "sightings" go unreported. There is no substitute for good, old-fashioned listening.

Figure 3-4—This is the OH9W/OH2AQ Radio Club 'DX Summit" WebCluster at *oh2aq.kolumbus.com/dxs/*. I've just requested a list of digital DX reports.

Chapter FOUR

PSK31

PSK31 was the brainchild of Peter Martinez, G3PLX, the father of AMTOR (see Chapter 1). He wanted to create a mode that was as easy to use as RTTY, yet much more robust in terms of weak-signal performance. Another important criterion was bandwidth. The HF digital subbands are narrow and tend to become crowded in a hurry (particularly during contests). Peter wanted to design a mode that would do all of its tricks within a very narrow bandwidth.

Experiments with PSK31 began in the mid-'90s. Amateurs at that time used *DOS* software and DSP development platforms such as the Texas Instruments TMS320C50DSK, Analog Devices ADSP21061 or Motorola DSP56002EVM. But in early 1999 Peter Martinez unveiled the first PSK31 software for *Windows*. The program required only a common 16-bit soundcard functioning as the analog-to-digital converter (and vice versa). With the large number of hams owning PCs equipped with soundcards, the popularity of PSK31 exploded.

WHAT IS PSK31?

First, let's dissect the name. The "PSK" stands for Phase Shift Keying, the modulation method that is used to generate the signal; "31" is the bit rate. Technically speaking, the bit rate is really 31.25, but "PSK31.25" isn't nearly as catchy.

Think of Morse code for a moment. It is a simple binary code expressed by short signal pulses (dits) and longer signal pulses (dahs). By combining strings of dits and dahs, we can communicate the entire English alphabet along with numbers and punctuation. Morse uses gaps of specific lengths to separate individual characters and words. Even beginners quickly learn to recognize these gaps; they don't need special signals to tell them that one character or word has ended and another is about to begin.

Now consider RTTY. We're still dealing with binary data (dits and dahs, if you will), but instead of on/off keying, we send the information by shifting frequencies. This is known as Frequency Shift Keying or FSK. One frequency represents a mark (1) and another represents a space (0). If you put enough mark and space signals together in proper order according to the RTTY code, you can send letters, numbers and a limited amount of punctuation.

The RTTY code shuffles various combinations of five bits to represent each character. For example, the letter A is expressed as 00011. To separate the individual characters RTTY must also add "start" and "stop" pulses (see Chapter 3).

For PSK31 Peter devised a new code that combines the best of RTTY and Morse. He christened his creation the Varicode because a varying number of bits are used for each character (see Table 4-1). Building on the example of Morse, Peter allocated the shorter codes to the letters that

Digipan pioneered the panoramic method of receiving PSK31 signals. Each line represents a PSK31 signal. You can copy individual signals by placing your mouse cursor on the line of your choice, then right clicking your mouse.

Table 4-1
The PSK31 Varicode

The codes are transmitted left bit first, with "0" representing a phase reversal on BPSK and "1" representing a steady carrier. A minimum of two zeros is inserted between characters. Some implementations may not handle all the codes below 32.

ASCII*	Varicode	ASCII*	Varicode	ASCII*	Varicode
0 (NUL)	1010101011	.	1010111	\	111101111
1 (SOH)	1011011011	/	110101111	]	111111011
2 (STX)	1011101101	0	10110111	^	1010111111
3 (ETX)	1101110111	1	10111101	_	101101101
4 (EOT)	1011101011	2	11101101	'	1011011111
5 (ENQ)	1101011111	3	11111111	A	1011
6 (ACK)	1011101111	4	101110111	B	1011111
7 (BEL)	1011111101	5	101011011	C	101111
8 (BS)	1011111111	6	101101011	D	101101
9 (HT)	11101111	7	110101101	e	11
10 (LF)	11101	8	110101011	f	111101
11 (VT)	1101101111	9	110110111	g	1011011
12 (FF)	1011011101	:	11110101	h	101011
13 (CR)	11111	;	110111101	i	1101
14 (SO)	1101110101	<	111101101	j	111101011
15 (SI)	1110101011	=	1010101	k	10111111
16 (DLE)	1011110101	>	110101011	l	11011
17 (DC1)	1011110101	?	1010101111	m	111011
18 (DC2)	1110101101	@	1010111101	n	1111
19 (DC3)	1110101111	A	1111101	o	111
20 (DC4)	1101011011	B	11101011	p	111111
21 (NAK)	1101101011	C	10101101	q	110111111
22 (SYN)	1101101101	D	10110101	r	10101
23 (ETB)	1101010111	E	1110111	s	10111
24 (CAN)	1101111111	F	11011011	t	101
25 (EM)	1101111101	G	11111101	u	110111
26 (SUB)	1110110111	H	101010101	v	1111011
27 (ESC)	1101010101	I	1111111	w	1101011
28 (FS)	1101011101	J	111111101	x	11011111
29 (GS)	1110111011	K	101111101	y	1011101
30 (RS)	1011111011	L	11010111	z	111010101
31 (US)	1101111111	M	10111011	{	1010110111
32 (SP)	1	N	11011101	|	110111011
!	111111111	O	10101011	}	1010110101
"	101011111	P	11010101	~	1011010111
#	111110101	Q	111011101	127	1110110101
$	111011011	R	10101111		
%	1011010101	S	1101111		
&	1010111011	T	1101101		
'	101111111	U	101010111		
(	11111011	V	110110101		
)	11110111	W	101011101		
*	101101111	X	101110101		
+	111011111	Y	101111011		
,	1110101	Z	1010101101		
-	110101	[	111110111		

*ASCII characters 0 through 32 are control codes. Their abbreviations are shown here in parentheses. For the meanings of the abbreviations, refer to any recent *ARRL Handbook*.

appeared most often in standard English text. The idea was to send the least number of bits possible during a given transmission. For example:

E is a very popular letter, so it gets a Varicode of 11
Z sees relatively little use, so its Varicode becomes 111010101

As with RTTY, however, we still need a way to signal the gaps between characters. The Varicode does this by using "00" to represent a gap. The Varicode is carefully structured so that two zeros never appear together in any of the combinations of 1s and 0s that make up the characters.

But how would the average ham generate a BPSK signal and transmit Varicode over the airwaves? Peter's answer was to use the DSP capabilities of the computer sound card to create an audio signal that shifted its phase angle 180° in sync with the 31.25 bit-per-second data stream. In Peter's scheme, a 0 bit in the data stream generates a phase shift, but a 1 does not. So, the software uses two phase angles (0° or "in phase" and 180° out of phase) to communicate 1s and 0s (see Figure 4-1). Because two phase angles are used to accomplish this, it is usually referred to as *binary phase-shift keying*, or BPSK.

Figure 4-1—A BPSK signal communicates binary information (0s and 1s) by shifting the signal phase 180°.

If you apply a BPSK audio signal to an SSB transceiver, you end up with BPSK modulated RF. At this data rate the resulting PSK31 RF signal is only 31.25 Hz wide, which is actually narrower than the average CW signal.

Concentrating your RF into a narrow bandwidth does wonders for reception, as any CW operator will tell you. But when you're trying to receive a BPSK-modulated signal, it is easier to recognize the phase transitions—even when they are deep in the noise—if your computer knows when to expect them. To accomplish this, the receiving station must synchronize with the transmitting station. Once they are in sync, the software at the receiving station "knows" when to look for data in the receiver's audio output. Every PSK31 transmission begins with a short "idle" string of 0s. This allows the receive software to get into sync right away. Thanks to the structure of the Varicode, however, the phase transitions are also mathematically predictable, so much so that the PSK31 software can quickly synchronize itself when you tune in during the middle of a transmission, or after you momentarily lose the signal.

The combination of narrow bandwidth, an efficient DSP algorithm and synchronized sampling creates a mode that can be received at very low signal levels. PSK31 rivals the weak-signal performance of CW and it is a vast improvement over RTTY.

Its terrific performance notwithstanding, PSK31 will not always provide 100% copy; it is as vulnerable to interference as any digital mode. And there are times, during a geomagnetic storm, for example, when ionospheric propagation will exhibit poor frequency stability. (When you are trying to receive a narrow-bandwidth, phase-shifting signal, frequency stability is very important.) This effect is almost always confined to the polar regions and it shows up as very rapid flutter, which is deadly to PSK31. The good news is that these events are usually short-lived.

BPSK and QPSK

Many people urged Peter to add some form of error correction to PSK31, but he initially resisted the idea because most error-correction schemes rely on transmitting redundant data bits. Adding more bits while still maintaining the desired throughput required a doubling of the data rate. If you double the BPSK data rate, the bandwidth doubles. As the bandwidth increases, the signal-to-noise ratio deteriorates and you get more errors. It's a sticky digital dilemma. How do you expand the information capacity of a BPSK channel without significantly increasing its bandwidth?

The Viterbi Competition and QPSK

The Viterbi is not so much a decoder as a whole family of encoders. Each one makes a different "guess" at what the last five transmitted QPSK data bits might have been. There are 32 different patterns of five bits and thus 32 encoders. At each step the phase-shift value predicted by the bit-pattern guess from each encoder is compared with the actual received phase-shift value, and the 32 encoders are given "marks out of 10" for accuracy. Just like in a knockout competition, the worst 16 are eliminated and the best 16 go on to the next round, taking their previous scores with them. Each surviving encoder then gives birth to "children," one guessing that the next transmitted bit will be a 0 and the other guessing that the next transmitted bit will be a 1. They all do their encoding to guess what the next phase shift will be, and are given marks out of 10 again that are added on to their earlier scores. The worst 16 encoders are killed off again and the cycle repeats.

It's a bit like Darwin's theory of evolution, and eventually all the descendants of the encoders that made the right guesses earlier will be among the survivors and will all carry the same "ancestral genes." We therefore just keep a record of the family tree (the bit-guess sequence) of each survivor, and can trace back to find the transmitted bit stream, although we have to wait at least five generations (bit periods) before all survivors have the same great great grandmother (who guessed right five bits ago). The whole point is that because the scoring system is based on the running total, the decoder always gives the most accurate guess—even if the received bit pattern is corrupted. In other words, the Viterbi decoder corrects errors.
—*Peter Martinez, G3PLX*

Peter finally found the answer by adding a second BPSK carrier at the transmitter with a 90° phase difference and a second demodulator at the receiver. The result is a signal that consists of four waveforms that differ in phase: they are each 90-degrees apart. Peter calls this quadrature polarity reversed keying, but it is better known as quaternary phase-shift keying or QPSK.

Splitting the transmitter power between two channels results in a 3-dB signal-to-noise penalty, but this is the same penalty you'd suffer if you doubled the bandwidth. Now that we have another channel to carry the redundant bits, we can use a convolutional encoder to generate one of four different phase shifts that correspond to patterns of five successive

WinPSK is another PSK31 program that uses the panoramic approach.

data bits. On the receiving end, we have a Viterbi decoder playing a very sophisticated guessing game. See the sidebar "The Viterbi Competition and QPSK."

Operating PSK31 in the QPSK mode will give you 100% copy under most conditions, but there is a catch. Tuning is twice as critical with QPSK as it is with BPSK. You have to tune the received signal within an accuracy of less than 4 Hz for the Viterbi decoder to detect the phase shifts and do its job. Obviously, both stations must be using very stable transceivers.

PSK31 SOFTWARE

The first step in setting up a PSK31 station is to jump onto the Web and download the software you need, according to the type of computer system you are using. As this book went to press there were PSK31 programs available for *Windows*, *Linux* and the Mac. The Resources section of this book has lists of Web addresses for software downloading.

Once you have the software safely tucked away on your hard drive, install it and read the "Help" files. Every PSK31 program has different features—too many to cover in this chapter. Besides, the features will no

Don't Overdrive Your Transceiver!

When you're setting up your rig for your first PSK31 transmission, the temptation is to adjust the output settings for "maximum smoke." This can be a serious mistake because overdriving your transceiver in PSK31 can result in a horrendous amount of splatter, which will suddenly make your PSK31 signal much wider than 31 Hz—and make you highly unpopular with operators on adjacent frequencies.

As you increase the transmit audio output from your soundcard or multimode processor, watch the ALC indicator on your transceiver. The ALC is the automatic level control that governs the audio drive level. When you see your ALC display indicating that audio limiting is taking place, you are feeding too much audio to the transceiver. The goal is to achieve the desired RF output with little or no activation of the ALC.

Unfortunately, monitoring the ALC by itself is not always a sure bet. Many radios can be driven to full output without budging the ALC meter. You'd think that it would be smooth sailing from there, but a number of rigs become decidedly nonlinear when asked to provide SSB output beyond a certain level (sometimes this nonlinearity can begin at the 50% output level). We can ignore the linearity issue to a certain extent with an SSB voice signal, but not with PSK31 because the immediate result, once again, is splatter.

So how can you tell if your PSK31 signal is clean? The simplest method is to ask someone to give you an evaluation on the air. The PSK31 programs that use a waterfall audio spectrum display can easily detect "dirty" signals. The splatter appears as rows of lines extending to the right and left of your primary signal. (Overdriven PSK31 signals may also have a harsh, clicking sound.)

If you are told that you are splattering, ask the other station to observe your signal as you slowly decrease the audio level from the soundcard or processor. When you reach the point where the splatter disappears, you're all set.

An alternative solution for *Windows* users is the PSKMeter by Software Science. This clever device samples the RF from your transceiver and *automatically* adjusts the audio output of your sound card until your signal is

doubt change substantially in the months and years that follow the publication of this book. The documentation that comes with your software is the best reference.

The Panoramic Approach

One of the early bugaboos of PSK31 had to do with tuning. Most PSK31 programs required you to tune your radio carefully, preferably in clean. The RF sampling port of the PSKMeter connects to your antenna coax with a **T** connector. The data is fed to your computer through an available COM (serial) port, or a USB port if you have a USB-to-serial converter. The PSKMeter software then analyzes the sampled signal and adjusts the master output volume of your sound card accordingly. The PSKMeter is available in kit form and can be ordered on the Web at **www.ssiserver.com/info/pskmeter/**.

Whether you choose automatic or manual adjustments, don't worry if you discover that you can only generate a clean signal at, say, 50 W output. With PSK31 the performance differential between 50 W and 100 W is inconsequential.—*Steve Ford, WB8IMY*

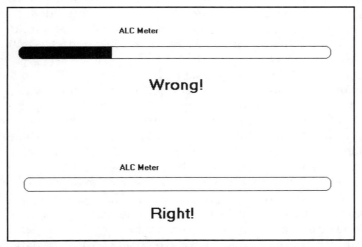

Examples of the right and wrong ways to adjust your transmit audio level. You should increase your transmit audio until the ALC meter just begins to move above zero, then *reduce* the volume to zero. If you are seeing any indication on your ALC meter when you are transmitting, you are driving your radio too hard and probably sending a distorted signal.

1-Hz increments. In the case of the original G3PLX software, for example, the narrow PSK31 signal would appear as a white trace on a thin waterfall display. Your goal was to bring the white trace directly into the center of the display, then tweak a bit more until the phase indicator in the circle above the waterfall was more-or-less vertical (or in the shape of a flashing cross if you were tuning at QPSK signal). Regardless of the software, PSK31 tuning required practice. You had to learn to recognize the sight

PSK31 Modulation and Demodulation

To transmit Varicode at a reasonable typing speed of about 50 words per minute needs a bit-rate of about 32 bps. In theory, we only need a bandwidth of 31.25 Hz to send this as binary data, and the frequency stability that this implies can be achieved with modern radio equipment on HF.

The method chosen was first used on the amateur bands, to my knowledge, by SP9VRC. Instead of frequency-shifting the carrier, which is wasteful of spectrum, or turning the carrier on and off, which is wasteful of transmitter power capability, the "dots" of the code are signaled by reversing the polarity of the carrier. You can think of this as equivalent to transposing the wires to your antenna feeder. This uses the transmitted signal more efficiently since we are comparing a positive signal before the reversal to a negative signal after it, rather than comparing the signal present in the dot to no-signal in the gap. But if we keyed the transmitter in this way at 31.25 baud, it would generate terrible key clicks, so we need to filter it.

If we take a string of dots in Morse code, and low-pass filter it to the theoretical minimum bandwidth, it will look the same as a carrier that is 100% amplitude-modulated by a sine wave at the dot rate. The spectrum is a central carrier and two sidebands at 6dB down on either side. A signal that is sending continuous reversals, filtered to the minimum bandwidth, is equivalent to a double-sideband suppressed-carrier emission, that is, to two tones either side of a suppressed carrier. The improvement in the performance of this polarity-reversal keying over on-off keying is thus equivalent to the textbook improvement in changing from amplitude-modulation telephony with full carrier to double-sideband with suppressed carrier. I have called this technique "polarity-reversal keying" so far, but everybody else calls it "binary phase-shift keying," or BPSK.

To generate BPSK in its simplest form, we could convert our data stream to levels of ±1 V, for example, take it through a low-pass filter and feed it into a balanced modulator.

The other input to the balanced modulator is the desired carrier frequency. When sending continuous reversals, this looks like a 1 V (P-P) sine wave going into a DSB modulator, so the output is a pure two-tone signal. In practice we use a standard SSB transceiver and perform the modulation at audio frequencies or carry out the equivalent process in a DSP chip. We could signal logic zero by continuous carrier and signal logic one by a reversal, but I do it the other way round for reasons that will become clear shortly.

There are many ways to demodulate BPSK, but they all start with a band-pass filter. For the speed chosen for PSK31, this filter can be as narrow as 31.25 Hz in theory. A brick-wall filter of precisely this width would be costly, however, not only in monetary terms but also in the delay time through the filter, and we want to avoid delays. A practical filter might be twice that width (62.5 Hz) at the 60-dB-down points with a delay-time of two bits (64 ms).

For the demodulation itself, since BPSK is equivalent to double sideband, the textbook method for demodulating DSB can be used. However, delaying the signal by one bit period and comparing it to the signal with no delay in a phase comparator can also demodulate it. The output is negative when the signal reverses polarity and positive when it doesn't.

We could extract the information from the demodulated signal by measuring the lengths of the "dots" and "dashes," as we do by ear with Morse code. It helps to pick the data out of the noise, however, if we know when to expect signal changes. We can easily transmit the data at an accurately timed rate, so it should be possible to predict when to sample the demodulator output. This process is known as synchronous reception, although the term "coherent" is sometimes wrongly used.

To synchronize the receiver to the transmitter, we can use the fact that a BPSK signal has an amplitude-modulation component. Although the modulation varies with the data pattern, it always contains a pure-tone component at the baud rate. This can be extracted using a narrow filter, a PLL or the DSP equivalent, and fed to the decoder to sample the demodulated data.

For the synchronization to work we need to make sure that there are no long gaps in the pattern of reversals. A completely steady carrier has no modulation, so we could never predict when the next reversal was due. Fortunately, Varicode is just what we need, provided we choose the logic levels so that zero corresponds to a reversal and one to a steady carrier. The idle signal of continuous zeros thus generates continuous reversals, giving us a strong 31.25-Hz modulation. Even with continuous keying, there will always be two reversals in the gaps between characters. The average number of reversals will therefore be more than two in every 6.5 bits, and there will never be more than 12 bits with no reversal at all. If we make sure that the transmission always starts with an idle period, then the timing will pull into sync quickly. By making the transmitter end a transmission with a "tail" of unmodulated carrier, it is then possible to use the presence or absence of reversals to squelch the decoder. Hence, the screen doesn't fill with noise when there is no signal.—*Peter Martinez, G3PLX* and sound of your target signal. With the weak warbling of PSK31, that wasn't always easy to do. And if your radio didn't tune in 1-Hz increments, the receiving task became even more difficult.

Nick Fedoseev, UT2UZ and Skip Teller, KH6TY, designed a solution and called it *DigiPan*. The "pan" in *DigiPan* stands for "panoramic"—a complete departure from the way most PSK31 programs work. With *DigiPan* the idea is to eliminate tedious tuning by detecting and displaying not just one signal, but entire groups of signals.

If you are operating your transceiver in SSB without using narrow IF or audio-frequency filtering, the bandwidth of the receive audio that you're dumping to your sound card is about 3000 Hz. With a bandwidth of only about 31 Hz, many PSK31 signals can squeeze into that spectrum. Panoramic software acts like an audio spectrum analyzer, continuously sweeping through the received audio from 100 to 3000 Hz and showing you the results in a large waterfall display that continuously scrolls from top to bottom. What you see on your monitor are vertical lines of various colors that indicate every signal that the software can detect. Bright lines represent strong signals while faint lines indicate weaker signals.

Other software writers jumped on the panoramic bandwagon and soon nearly every PSK31 program used waterfall displays of one type or another. The beauty of panoramic reception is that you do not have to tune your radio to monitor any of the signals you see in the waterfall. You simply move your mouse cursor to the signal of your choice and click. A cursor appears on the trace and the software begins displaying text. You can hop from one signal to another in less than a second merely by clicking your mouse. If you discover someone calling CQ and you want to answer, click on the transmit button and away you go—no radio adjustments necessary.

The Panoramic Downside

The weakness of panoramic reception is found in the fact that your receiver is running "wide open." The only IF filtering is typically your 1.8 or 2.5 kHz SSB filter. The automatic gain control, or AGC, circuit in your receiver is acting on everything within that bandwidth, working hard to raise or lower the overall gain according to the overall signal strength. That's fine if all the PSK31 signals are approximately the same strength, but if a very strong signal appears within the bandwidth, the AGC will *reduce* the gain to compensate.

The result will be that many of the signals in the waterfall display will suddenly vanish, or become very weak, as the AGC drops the receiver

PSK63—The High-Speed Cousin of PSK31

In 2003, a new variant of PSK31 appeared on the HF digital stage. It was the creation of Skip Teller, KH6TY, and is known as *PSK63*.

This mode is intended to be a higher-speed version of PSK31 for contest and DX applications. PSK63 boasts a 100-WPM character transmission speed, which is faster than most people can type, and considerably faster than RTTY.

Although it is faster than PSK31, the bandwidth of a typical PSK63 signal is limited to about 65 Hz, which is 1/5 the bandwidth of a RTTY signal. PSK63 requires much less power than RTTY for the same communications performance.

As this book went to press, several multimode software packages had incorporated PSK63, and PSK63 signals were popping up on the air. Because of the somewhat wider bandwidth, PSK63 operators are warned not to use the mode in proximity to PSK31 signals. The custom is to use PSK63 at the upper end of common PSK31 frequency groups. For example, PSK63 on 20 meters is usually heard around 14073 kHz, well above the customary PSK31 territory between 14070 and 14072 kHz.

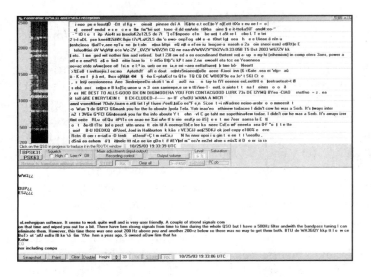

MultiPSK is an example of software than can send and receive several different modes, including PSK31 and PSK63. In this image, it is attempting to decode 24 signals at the same time. Most are just gibberish "noise," but several are actual PSK31 conversation. The waterfall is visible along the left-hand side of the window.

gain. In cases where an extremely strong signal appears, *all* signals except the rock crusher may disappear completely.

Some PSK31 operators are using transceivers that allow them to enable 500-Hz CW filters when the rig is in the SSB mode. They'll switch in the filters and sacrifice their wide waterfall displays to remove strong signals nearby.

TUNING PSK31

Most of the PSK31 activity can be found on 20 meters around **14070 kHz**, but you'll also find PSK31 on the following frequencies:

3580 kHz
7070 kHz
10140 kHz
21070 kHz
28120 kHz

Start by parking your radio on the frequency of your choice and booting up your PSK31 software. *Do not touch your rig's VFO again.* Why not?

The frequency your transceiver displays in the SSB mode is the *suppressed carrier frequency*. If you've selected upper sideband on your radio (USB), your receiver range is everything from the suppressed carrier frequency to about 2 or 3 kHz above it. If you select lower sideband (LSB), your receiver range extends 2 or 3 kHz *below* the suppressed carrier frequency.

For example, let's say that you've dialed your transceiver to 14070 kHz and you have the radio in USB mode. Assuming that you don't have a narrow IF filter enabled, your receiver is picking up everything from 14070 to about 14073 kHz. The PSK31 software will display all signals within that range. Just place your mouse cursor on one of the vertical signal lines and right click. The software selects and decodes that signal without the need for you to tune your radio. When you transmit, the PSK31 software generates a tone that corresponds to the tone of the signal you selected. When that tone is applied to your radio, it creates an RF signal on the correct frequency. That's all there is to it!

PSK31 signals have a distinctive sound unlike any digital mode you've heard on the ham bands. You won't find PSK31 by listening for the deedle-deedle of a RTTY signal, and PSK31 doesn't "chirp" like the

RF Feedback and Sound Cards

One of the most common problems encountered when using a sound card as a PSK31 modem is RF feedback. Sound cards are not designed for Amateur Radio, and can suffer from high levels of RF, usually getting into the card via the audio input and/or output cables from the transceiver. The RF causes nonlinear rectification in the sound card circuitry, and the envelope of the rectified RF is fed, as audio, to the transmitter again. This creates a loop which can result in a parasitic oscillation on the audio output of the sound card, and hence also on the transmitter output. It usually takes the form of an extra tone that is exactly one-half of the wanted output audio. Thus, if the sound card is outputting 1000Hz, the spurious is 500Hz and just sounds like an added richness to the sound. Alternatively the feedback may just create a jumble of noise.

The way to check for RF feedback is to listen to the sound card output as you are transmitting, not by turning up the speakers (which may not be suffering), but by connecting headphones across the line to the transmitter. First listen with the transmitter off radiating, then see if there's any "added richness" in the sound as you switch the transmitter on and wind up the power. You may find, if there is RF feedback, that at a certain power level there is a sudden change in the sound as the parasitic oscillation starts.

Another way to detect RF feedback is if you have an old wavemeter with a headphone socket, intended originally for checking the audio of an AM transmitter. Alternatively you can make one yourself with just a pair of headphones and a single diode. The idea is simply to detect any amplitude modulation on the transmitter output. A clean transmission will give no sound at all (no amplitude modulation) when radiating a "tune" carrier, and a very low-frequency buzz (31.25Hz) when idling. RF feedback will give you a tone in the headphones that starts suddenly as you wind up the power past the critical parasitic-oscillation point. The cure is usually to stop the RF getting down the audio cable from the transmitter to the sound card. Ferrite rings, with both the audio input and audio output wrapped together through the ring as many times as you can, will usually fix it. It's possible that the PTT cable from the transmitter to the COM port will need treating in the same way.—*Peter Martinez, G3PLX*

PACTOR interference, as seen with *DigiPan* software. In this example there is a very strong PACTOR signal (in the center of the waterfall display) and another weaker PACTOR signal nearby.

TOR modes. PSK31 signals *warble*.

Using waterfall displays you may often see (and copy) PSK31 signals that you cannot otherwise hear. It is not at all uncommon to see several strong signals (the audible ones) interspersed with wispy blue ghosts of very weak "silent" signals. Click on a few of these ghosts and you may be rewarded with text (not error-free, but good enough to understand what is being discussed).

Does the Sideband Matter?

With BPSK, the most popular PSK31 mode by far, the answer is "no." You can have your transceiver in upper or lower sideband and work any signals that appear in your software display.

QPSK is another matter. Sideband selection *is* critical for QPSK. Most QPSK operators choose upper sideband, although lower sideband would work just as well. The point is that both stations must be using the *same* sideband, whether it's upper or lower.

A PSK31 CONVERSATION

Conversing with PSK31 is identical to RTTY. For example:

Yes, John, I'm seeing perfect text on my screen, but I can barely hear your signal. PSK31 is amazing! KF6I DE WB8IMY K

KF6I waits for WB8IMY's transmission to end, toggles his software to the transmit mode, and begins typing . . .

I know what you mean, Steve. You are also weak on my end, but 100% copy.

Some PSK31 programs and processor software offer type-ahead buffers, which allow you to compose your response "off line" while you are reading the incoming text from the other station.

Almost all programs offer pre-programmed messages known as *macros*. A macro allows you create a sequence of actions that will take place whenever you press a particular key on your keyboard. Every program uses different macro symbols, but here is a typical example...

```
<TX>
CQ CQ CQ CQ CQ CQ DE WB8IMY WB8IMY
CQ CQ CQ CQ CQ CQ DE WB8IMY WB8IMY K
<RX>
```

Whenever you press the assigned key, this macro will place your radio in the transmit mode <TX>, send two lines of CQ text, then switch your radio back to the receive mode <RX>. CQ macros are common because they streamline the process of calling a CQ.

Depending on your software, you may be able to set up more elaborate macros, like this one...

```
<TX>
<HISCALL> DE WB8IMY. Thank you for the call. Your signal
report is <SIGNALRPT>. My QTH is Wallingford, CT, USA. Back to
you. <HISCALL> DE WB8IMY K
<RX>
```

The macro starts by placing the transceiver into the transmit mode

<TX>. <HISCALL> inserts the call sign of the calling station (assuming that you've entered it into the software's log) and then begins sending text. The signal report <SIGNALRPT> is inserted automatically. Finally, <HISCALL> appears again as you turn it back to him and return your radio to the receive mode <RX>.

Be careful about relying too much on macros. They are convenient, but they can also cause confusion if used improperly. In addition, some hams create macros that contain lengthy descriptions of their station equipment, families, etc. It's tempting to tap that macro key and sit back while your computer sends more information than the other person really wants to know!

Chapter FIVE

PACTOR

Hans-Peter Helfert, DL6MAA, and Ulrich Strate, DF4KV, developed PACTOR in 1991. It remains to this day the most popular of the HF *burst* modes. There are now three versions of PACTOR: PACTOR I, PACTOR II and PACTOR III. PACTOR I is considered obsolete and is little used. PACTOR II and III are in current use, primarily to connect to automated stations such as the WinLink 2000 network (see the next chapter). The good news is that most PACTOR II and III controllers are configured to accept PACTOR I connections.

We call PACTOR a burst mode because of the way it sends information. Rather than sending a continuous stream of data like RTTY, PSK31, MFSK16 or Hellschreiber, PACTOR transmits bursts of information that take the form of short data blocks. When the data is received intact, the receiving station sends an ACK signal (for acknowledgment). If the data contains errors, a NAK is sent (for nonacknowledgment). In simple terms, ACK means, "I've received the last group of characters okay. Send the next group." NAK means, "There are errors in the last group of characters, send them again." This back-and-forth data conversation sounds like crickets chirping. In the case of PACTOR, the long chirp is the data and the short chirp is the ACK or NAK.

MEMORY ARQ

In less sophisticated burst modes such as AMTOR or packet, a data block must be repeated over and over if that's what it takes to deliver the information error-free. This results in slow communication, especially when conditions are poor.

PACTOR handles the challenge of "repairing" errors in an interesting way. Each data block is sent and acknowledged with an ACK signal if it's received intact. If signal fading or interference destroys some of the data, a NAK is sent and the block is repeated. Nothing new so far—packet and AMTOR behave much the same way. The big difference, however, involves memory.

When a PACTOR controller receives a mangled character block, it analyzes the parts and temporarily memorizes whatever information appears to be error-free. If the block is shot full of holes on the next transmission as well, the controller quickly compares the new data fragments with what it has memorized. It fills the gaps as much as possible and then, if necessary, asks for another repeat. Eventually, the controller gathers enough fragments to construct the entire block (see **Figure 5-1**). PACTOR's memory ARQ feature dramatically reduces the need to make repeat transmissions of damaged data. This translates into much higher throughput.

PACTOR has the capability to communicate at varying speeds according to band conditions. PACTOR throughput is enhanced by using Huffman coding that reduces the average character length for improved efficiency. **Table 5-1** shows the Huffman compressed equivalent of each ASCII character used in PACTOR, with the least significant bit (LSB) given first. The length of individual characters varies from 2 to 15 bits, with the most frequently used characters being the shortest. This results in an average character length of 4 to 5 bits for English text, instead of the 8 bits required for normal ASCII.

Figure 5-1—Memory ARQ at work. WB8IMY sends data to WB8ISZ (A), but bits 2, 5 and 6 are corrupted. The controller at WB8ISZ's station memorizes the good data as well as the positions of the corrupted bits. It sends a NAK (B) to demand a repeat of all the data. On the next transmission (C), bits 1, 3 and 4 are corrupted, but that's not a problem. WB8ISZ's controller has these bits stored in memory from the first transmission. What's important is the fact that bits 2, 5 and 6 made it through intact. They're the missing bits from the first transmission. These bits are combined with the ones in memory and the entire data segment is complete! WB8ISZ now sends an ACK (D) for the next batch. (A PACTOR data segment is actually 192 bits long when operating at 200 bit/s; 80 bits long at 100 bit/s.)

Table 5-1
PACTOR Huffman Compression

Char	ASCII	Huffman (LSB [sent first] on left)
space	32	10
e	101	011
n	10	0101
i	105	1101
r	114	1110
t	116	00000
s	115	00100
d	100	00111
a	97	01000
u	117	11111
l	108	000010
h	104	000100
g	103	000111
m	109	001011
<CR>	13	001100
<LF>	10	001101
o	111	010010
c	99	010011
b	98	0000110
f	102	0000111
w	119	0001100
D	68	0001101
k	107	0010101
z	122	1100010
.	46	1100100
,	44	1100101
S	83	1111011
A	65	00101001
E	69	11000000
P	112	11000010
v	118	11000011
O	48	11000111
F	70	11001100
B	66	11001111
C	67	11110001
I	73	11110010
T	84	11110100
O	79	000101000
P	80	000101100
1	49	001010000
R	82	110000010
(	40	110011011
)	41	110011100
L	76	110011101
N	78	111100000
Z	90	111100110
M	77	111101010

Char	ASCII	Huffman (LSB [sent first] on left)
9	57	0001010010
W	87	0001010100
5	53	0001010101
y	121	0001010110
2	50	0001011010
3	51	0001011011
4	52	0001011100
6	54	0001011101
7	55	0001011110
8	56	0001011111
H	72	0010100010
J	74	1100000110
U	85	1100000111
V	86	1100011000
<FS>	28	1100011001
x	120	1100011010
K	75	1100110100
?	63	1100110101
=	61	1111000010
q	113	1111010110
Q	81	1111010111
j	106	00010100110
G	71	00010100111
-	45	00010101111
:	58	00101000111
!	33	11110011101
/	47	11110011110
*	42	001010001100
"	34	110001101100
%	37	110001101101
Ô	39	110001101110
_	95	111100001100
&	38	111100111001
+	43	111100111110
>	62	111100111111
@	64	0001010111000
$	36	0001010111001
<	60	0001010111010
X	88	0001010111011
#	35	0010100011011
Y	89	00101000110101
;	59	11110000110100
	92	11110000110101
[	91	001010001101000
]	93	001010001101000
<DEL>	127	110001101111000
~	126	110001101111001
}	125	110001101111010

[continued on next page]

Char	ASCII	Huffman (LSB [sent first] on left)
	124	110001101111011
{	123	110001101111100
Ò	96	110001101111101
^	94	110001101111110
<US>	31	110001101111111
<GS>	29	111100001101100
<ESC>	27	111100001101101
<EM>	25	111100001101110
<CAN>	24	111100001101111
<ETB>	23	111100001110000
<SYN>	22	111100001110001
<NAK>	21	111100001110010
<DC4>	20	111100001110011
<DC3>	19	111100001110100
<DC2>	18	111100001110101
<DC1>	17	111100001110110
<DLE>	16	111100001110111
<RS>	30	111100001111000
<SI>	15	111100001111001
<SO>	14	111100001111010
<FF>	12	111100001111011
<VT>	11	111100001111100
<HT>	9	111100001111101
<BS>	8	111100001111110
<BEL>	7	111100001111111
<ACK>	6	111100111000000
<ENQ>	5	111100111000001
<EOT>	4	111100111000010
<ETX>	3	111100111000011
<STX>	2	111100111000100
<SOH>	1	111100111000101
<NUL>	0	111100111000110
<SUB>	26	111100111000111

WHAT DO YOU NEED TO RUN PACTOR?

Assembling a PACTOR station is very simple. All you need are the following:

• An SSB transceiver. PACTOR uses a two-tone mark/space system similar to RTTY. This means that PACTOR can be sent with AFSK, with transmit audio applied at the microphone or accessory jack, or with FSK, where the transmitter generates the mark/space frequency shifts by itself. If you operate in AFSK, it doesn't matter which sideband you use, upper or lower.

• A data terminal or a computer running terminal software

• A multimode communications processor (MCP) with PACTOR capability. Most MCPs include PACTOR I, but only controllers manufactured by Special Communications Systems (SCS) offer PACTOR II and III.

When assembling your PACTOR station, use the guidelines discussed in Chapter 2. You'll notice that I haven't mentioned using a sound card modem for PACTOR. There is sound card software such as *MixW* (**www.mixw.net**) that will allow you to receive PACTOR I transmissions, but nothing is available to receive *and* transmit any of the PACTOR modes.

CQ PACTOR

Although most PACTOR activity involves connecting to automated systems, you can still occasionally enjoy a "live" conversation.

You call CQ on PACTOR using forward error correction, or FEC. The FEC signal sounds like very fast RTTY, but in reality it is a stream of data in which each character is repeated twice for redundancy—there are no ACKs or NAKs. Obviously, this means that an FEC transmission is not error-free, but the copy is good enough to pull out the call sign of the sending station. When you're sending a PACTOR CQ, that's really all that matters.

If you hear a signal that you suspect is a PACTOR FEC CQ, tune carefully until your MCP indicates that it has locked (synchronized) with the FEC signal. Within a short time, you should begin to see text on your screen.

CQ CQ CQ DE WB8IMY WB8IMY WB8IMY
CQ CQ CQ DE WB8IMY WB8IMY WB8IMY
CQ CQ CQ DE WB8IMY WB8IMY WB8IMY K K

Notice that this CQ uses several short lines of text rather than a few long lines. This helps stations synchronize more easily.

STARTING A CONVERSATION

Answering a CQ in PACTOR is straightforward. Depending on the software you're using, it may be as simple as entering:

CALL N1BKE
or, CONNECT N1BKE

...at the cmd: prompt. Some types of software streamline the process even further. There may be pop-up boxes where you simply enter a call sign.

Once you make contact, the conversation proceeds in turns. This means that one station "talks" (the ISS or information sending station) while the other "listens" (the IRS or information receiving station). When the ISS has had his say, he sends a special control signal known as the *over* command that immediately reverses the roles—suddenly you are the ISS and he is the IRS. Introduce yourself and ask a question about where he lives, or what he does for a living. Use the over command to flip the link again. A conversation is underway!

Depending on the software you are using with your MCP, sending the over command is usually as easy as tapping a single key. The software usually provides some sort of visual indicator to show which mode you are in—IRS or ISS—in case you become confused! If you forget to send the over command, your stations will simply sit there and chirp mindlessly at each other. Fortunately, the IRS can send an over command and flip the link for you if necessary. This is known as a "forced over."

PACTOR II

You can think of PACTOR II in terms of being a supercharged version of PACTOR I. In good conditions, PACTOR II boasts a data transfer rate up to six times faster than PACTOR. At the same time, PACTOR II is capable of maintaining links in conditions where the signal-to-noise ratio is at -18 dB. This means that PACTOR II can carry on an exchange even when the signals are virtually inaudible. Such remarkable performance is also conservative when it comes to bandwidth; a PACTOR II signal only occupies about 500 Hz of spectrum.

The complex pi/4-DQPSK modulation system used by PACTOR II requires DSP technology and fast microprocessors. With DSP, you let the software decide the composition of the signal, not the hardware. DSP is much more flexible, allowing you to create the signal you want without having to worry about hardware filters and so on. The tradeoff is that you must use high-speed microprocessors to handle all the incoming and outgoing information at a decent rate.

PACTOR II is also backward compatible with PACTOR I. That is, a PACTOR II operator can communicate with a PACTOR I operator and vice versa.

PACTOR II is only available in the PTC-II series multimode processors manufactured (or licensed) by SCS. In addition to PACTOR II, the PTC-II offers other HF modes such as RTTY, SSTV, packet and even PSK31.

PACTOR II STATION REQUIREMENTS AND OPERATION

The requirements for a PACTOR II station are essentially the same as for a PACTOR station: An SSB transceiver, a computer or data terminal, and a PTC-II or PTC-IIe processor.

PACTOR II also operates in nearly the same fashion as PACTOR I. In fact, the link is initially established using the PACTOR I protocol, then automatically switched to PACTOR II if both stations are using PACTOR II processors. And as with PACTOR I, you must take turns during the conversation, sending an over command to allow the other operator to send data.

DISSECTING A PACTOR DATA PACKET

A PACTOR data packet is either 96 bits long sent at 100 baud, or 192 bits long sent at 200 baud, with the data rate dependent on conditions. Each packet consists of a Header byte, Data field, and Status byte, followed by the CRC byte given twice. The Header byte consists of the 8-bit pattern for 55 hexadecimal and is used for synchronization, Memory-ARQ, and listen mode. The Data field contains 64 bits if sent at 100 baud, or 160 bits if sent at 200 baud. Its format is normally Huffman-compressed ASCII, with conventional 8-bit ASCII as the alternative. The Status byte provides the packet count, data format (whether standard 8-bit ASCII or Huffman-compressed ASCII), break-in request, and QRT bit, for a total of 8 bits. The CRC calculation is based on the ITU-T polynomial $xE16+xE12+xE5+1$. The CRC byte is calculated for the whole packet starting with the data field, without Header, and consists of 16 bits.

(from the April 2000 issue of *QST*)

The SCS PTC-IIe is the smaller sized, and smaller priced, brother of the PTC-II controller. The PTC and PTC-IIe are the only MCPs that offer PACTOR II—and the PTC-IIe is the only MCP to date that includes PSK31 in its list of modes. (The PTC-IIx was introduced in 2003.)

The PTC-IIe's PACTOR II performance was astonishing. In several instances we successfully accessed BBSs under abominable conditions where we could scarcely hear the other station's signals in the noise. With PACTOR II the data flowed smoothly, albeit more slowly in the midst of deep fades. On the basis of on-air tests, the PTC-IIe implementation of PACTOR II clearly outperformed G-TOR. When we put it up against Clover II, however, the differences were less obvious. In fact, it was impossible to determine a "winner" between the two modes.

In PSK31 the PTC-IIe was mediocre. We matched it head-to-head against sound card-based PSK31 software and the sound cards came out on top every time. Part of the problem may have involved the level of tuning precision required for PSK31. The PTC-IIe uses its multisegment LED bargraph in an interesting way, adjusting the intensity of the segments until the center three are glowing brightest when the PSK31 signal is properly tuned. Clever as this may be, it seemed as though we were able to achieve more accurate tuning, and better copy, using the more common PSK31 software "waterfall" displays. RTTY performance was very good, better than either the KAM '98 or PK232DSP, but not quite as sharp as the HAL DXP38. One of our reviewers tried the PTC-IIe during the 2000 ARRL RTTY roundup and was impressed with its ability to copy weak signals in strong interference. The PTC-IIe works strictly in AFSK; it does not provide an FSK output.

The PTC-IIe offers both HF and VHF packet, but the manual is vague about this feature. It spends several pages discussing 300-baud (HF) packet—correctly disdaining it as a poor mode for HF work—with hardly a mention of 1200-baud (VHF) packet. With a little experimentation we had

PACTOR II FRAMES

The basic PACTOR-II frame structure is similar to PACTOR-I. It consists of a header, a data field, the status byte and the CRC. The standard cycle duration is 1.25 seconds—the same as PACTOR. Even so, the lengths of the control signals, such as the ACKs and NAKs, were the PTC-IIe working nicely at 1200 baud. The only drawback is that the unit is not GPS compatible for use with the Automatic Position Reporting System.

The DSP filtering function of the PTC-IIe can be put to work for other applications. By entering the Audio mode you can use the PTC-IIe in the same way you would an external DSP audio filter. We fed the audio to an amplifier and listened as we experimented with the notch filter, noise filter, etc. All adjustments are made from the keyboard. This is a nifty feature for those times when you'd like to take a break from digital and work a little phone or CW.

Speaking of CW, yes, the PTC-IIe does that, too. Once again, the copy ability was similar to the other MCPs we tested. The PTC-IIe also does SSTV and fax, but for these modes it functions more like a modem and requires external software to do the actual signal processing and display. Installation of the PTC-IIe is fairly simple. On the rear panel there is a DIN jack for the audio in/out and transceiver keying lines. Connect the lines as shown in the manual and you are in business. Audio output levels are controlled through software commands.

The English manual has been translated well from the original German, but the organization is poor. It is not easy to locate the information you need, and you often find it lacking in detail. The software provided with the PTC-IIe is DOS only, and it performed reasonably well. At this price level, however, we had expected to find a full-featured Windows program.

The PTC-IIe is targeted to a particular market: the traveling hams. These folks cruise the roads for months in recreational vehicles or roam the seas in private boats. Many of these travelers depend on the global WinLink 2000 network to stay in touch via Internet e-mail. So, it is important to have a high-performance PACTOR I/PACTOR II MCP that can maintain connections under the worst conditions. When e-mail is one of your lifelines to friends and loved ones, price is less of a consideration than quality. For the average housebound ham, $649 may be too steep to justify—even for the remarkable performance of PACTOR II. For the traveling amateur, however, that price tag is quite reasonable.

increased somewhat to improve reliability under poor conditions. As a result, the length of the data packet had to be shortened to 800 ms so that everything would still "fit" within the 1.25-second cycle. PACTOR II also has a "long path" mode similar to PACTOR I where the cycle is stretched to accommodate signal returns from very distant stations.

Unlike PACTOR I, PACTOR II can switch to longer packets if the data blocks are not filled up with idles (i.e., if the transmitter buffer indicates that more information has to be transferred than fitting into the standard packets). If the information sending station (ISS) prefers to use long packets, it automatically sets the long-cycle flag in the status word. The information receiving station (IRS) then can accept the change and away you go! Now the data field can contain as many as 2208 bits of information. These data packets are 3.28 seconds in length—quite large by HF digital standards—and the entire cycle duration switches to 3.75 seconds. This mode is primarily used when you are exchanging large files with another station.

PACTOR II DATA COMPRESSION

PACTOR I and PACTOR II both use automatic on-line Huffman data compression. PACTOR II, however, also uses run-length encoding and Pseudo-Markov Compression (PMC). Compared to 8-bit ASCII (plain text), PMC yields a compression factor of around 1.9, which leads to an effective speed of about 600 bits per second in average propagation conditions in data mode. The PACTOR II processor automatically evaluates the condition of the link from moment to moment and selects PMC, Huffman encoding or the original ASCII code, whichever is best at the time.

Ordinary Huffman compression exploits the one-dimensional probability distribution of the characters in plain texts. The more frequently a character occurs, the shorter the Huffman symbol assigned to it. Markov compression, on the other hand, can be considered as a "double" Huffman compression because for each preceding character, a probability distribution of the next character can be calculated. For example, if the actual character is "e," it is very likely that "i" or "s" occurs next, but extremely unlikely that a "w" follows.

As you can probably guess, Markov coding would require an enormously large and complex lookup table—well beyond the capacity of a stand-alone communications processor! That is why SCS chose Pseudo Markov Coding. With PMC the Markov encoding is limited to the 16 most frequent preceding characters. All other characters trigger normal Huffman compression of the next character. This reduces the Markov coding table to a reasonable size and makes the character probabilities less critical.

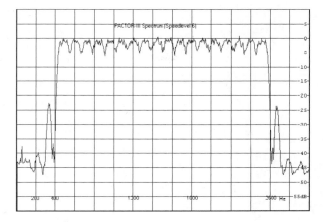

Figure 5-2. A typical PACTOR III waveform.

PACTOR III

PACTOR III is the next step in PACTOR evolution. It was introduced by SCS in 2001 as a firmware upgrade to their PTC line of multimode controllers. When this edition went to press, PACTOR III was being used primarily in the WinLink 2000 network, although upgraded controllers remain "backward compatible" with PACTOR I and II.

PACTOR III represents a substantial improvement with its 2-dimensional orthogonal pulse shaping, advanced error control coding, and efficient source coding. It provides excellent performance in poor signal conditions and achieves high throughput rates under good signal conditions. The tradeoff, however, is the fact that a PACTOR III signal occupies a 2200-Hz bandwidth, as much as a typical SSB voice transmission (see **Figure 5-2**). For this reason, PACTOR III stations often operate well above the frequencies used for PSK31, RTTY and other modes. For example, on 20 meters you will hear PACTOR III signals between 14103 and 14115 kHz.

The key benefits of PACTOR III are:

• Higher throughput compared to PACTOR II. Under average signal conditions, a speed gain factor of 3-4 is possible. Under very good conditions, PACTOR III can be as much as 5 times faster.

• A maximum data rate of 2700 bits per second without compression. With text compression applied, a data rate of 5200 bps is possible.

As with PACTOR II, you must purchase an SCS multimode controller to use PACTOR III. This mode is not available from any other manufacturers.

Chapter SIX

Winlink 2000

By Steve Waterman, K4CJX

The Internet has become the message information medium of choice for most hams, but there is a sizeable group of amateurs who often travel beyond the reach of the Internet. This group includes hams at sea, travelers in recreational vehicles (RVs), missionaries, scientists, explorers and emergency management applications such as ARES and RACES. No doubt the day will come when wireless, affordable high-speed Internet access will be available from any point on the globe. Until that day arrives, however, the Winlink 2000 Amateur Radio digital network is the most capable existing media for Internet access, and it will do this worldwide. Winlink 2000 has been described as "what the worldwide packet radio networks wanted to be, but never attained."

THE EVOLUTION OF WINLINK 2000

More than 40 HF digital stations worldwide have formed a remarkably efficient Internet information exchange network, including e-mail, binary file transfer and global graphic weather reporting and how-to bulletins. Running Winlink 2000 software and using the three PACTOR protocols, these facilities transfer information between HF stations and the Internet. They also share information among themselves using Internet forwarding.

In addition, most recently, over 150 VHF/UHF packet-to-Internet "Telpac" stations have joined the HF digital network stations, mostly for emergency preparedness purposes, to cover the "last mile" for their local regions.

A world map of WinLink 2000 stations.

The network evolved in the mid 1990s from the original AMTOR-based APLink system, authored by Victor D. Poor, W5SMM. APLink was a network of stations that relayed messages to and from each other and the VHF packet network (and Winlink 2000 still does this where VHF/UHF Packet exists.) As PCs became more powerful, and as the PACTOR protocols superceded AMTOR, a new software system was needed. That need brought about the debut of Winlink Classic, authored by Poor, with additions from Peter Schultz, TY1PS. Winlink itself evolved with substantial enhancements courtesy of Hans Kessler, N8PGR. To bring the Internet into the picture Winlink stations needed an e-mail agent to interface with cyberspace. To meet that requirement Steve Waterman, K4CX enlisted the help of Jim Jennings, W5EUT and Rick Muething, KN6KB, to add Netlink to Winlink Classic.

WINLINK 2000 TODAY

Early in 2000, the system took a major technological and evolutionary leap, becoming a full-featured Internet-to-HF "star network" gateway system known as Winlink 2000 or "WL2K." Winlink 2000 is an International network of participating stations

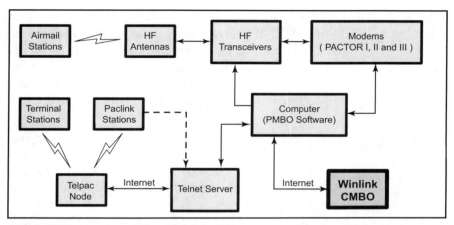

A simplified diagram of the WinLink 2000 system operation. The actual system may have 40+ HF PMBOs and 100+ Telpac VHF/UHF nodes. All forwarding between system participants is via Internet TCP/IP or Telnet. For simplicity no user connections are shown.

(PMBOs on HF and Telpac on VHF/UHF), all connected to a central server (CMBO), which is the hub for Internet connectivity to Internet e-mail, bulletins and position reporting.

Jim Corenman, KE6RK, concurrently developed software called *AirMail*, which is the end-user or "client" portion of Winlink 2000 on HF. On UHF/VHF, Winlink also hosts a Telpac module used with its end-user program, *Paclink*. These two modules are used together for short-range communication.

Thank to these advancements, as an example, HF digital operator at sea can now connect to a Winlink 2000 participating network station using *AirMail*, and exchange Internet e-mail with non-ham friends and family. He can also exchange messages with other amateurs by using the Winlink 2000 network stations as a traditional global mailbox operation. There are also over 700 NOAA and other text-based and graphic weather products available on request, which, of course, adds immeasurably to the safety and well being of the maritime ham. Likewise, with the use of Telpac and *Paclink*, local areas may be easily covered for emergency communications where the accuracy of written documents are necessary or desirable.

Most Winlink 2000 participating stations scan a variety of HF digital frequencies on a regular basis, listening on each frequency for about two seconds. By scanning through frequencies on several bands, the Winlink 2000 stations can be accessed on whichever band is available at any given time. At the time of this writing, 14 out of the existing 40 PMBOs use multiple radios in order to reduce the amount of scan cycle time for their stations, allowing multiple simultaneous connections resulting in a much greater throughput for the entire system.

REDUCTION IN USE OF THE HF RADIO SPECTRUM

One important design objective of the Winlink development team was to reduce the use of the HF spectrum to only that required to exchange messages with a radio end-user, and to do that at full "machine" speeds. In many parts of the world, the HF spectrum is very crowded, especially on 20, 30 and 40 meters. By limiting the forwarding of messages between WL2K PMBOs through the Central Server (CMBO) to the Internet, a great deal of HF air time is eliminated making our valuable spectrum available to individual radio users either for message handling or for other operations. Efficient use of the Amateur Radio spectrum is paramount in the WL2K process as it should be in any Amateur radio application.

ELIMINATION OF THE NEED FOR A HOME PMBO WITH THE USE OF "INTELLIGENT ROUTING"

Another important design objective of Winlink 2000 was to eliminate the traditional need to designate a specific "home" PMBO for an end- user (although he may optionally continue to such a designation). WL2K uses a message routing system the makes note of which Winlink PMBO stations a user has connected over a 90 day period. Whenever a message is received for a user, it is forwarded to these specific PMBOs. When the message is read at any one of these PMBOs, an internal notice is automatically sent to those specific PMBOs used by the particular user, indicating that the message was delivered, thereby, allowing it to be removed from any PMBO pending message list.

REGISTERING AS A WINLINK RADIO USER

When you first check into one of the PMBOs, your call sign will be accepted on a temporary basis until your license is automatically or manually verified for proper HF operation. If your call sign is from a country that does not have a publicly listed "official" database of Amateur Radio calls, then you will be asked to scan and e-mail or fax a copy of your license in order to remain a Winlink 2000 user. Otherwise, you will just be automatically instated within a short period of time. Alternatively, a user may ask any WL2K PMBO sysop to enter their call into the system database, and indicate the h-route of any MBO external to WL2K. If there is no record of a user's call in the system database then messages are forwarded to him based on the included h-route.

MESSAGE DELIVERY

For normal, non-emergency operations, users are automatically registered and their call signs verified simply by connecting to any WL2K PMBO. If a user checks into a PMBO for the first time, the system makes note of it and forwards all pending messages to that PMBO. The next time the user connects to that PMBO, any of his pending messages will be there. Messages will continue to come to all PMBOs that have registered the user. Should the user not check into a particular PMBO for 90 days, messages to the user will cease coming to that PMBO. This is of great benefit to mobile amateurs such as RVers, cruising vessels, and amateurs in remote locations that travel. It also keeps only those PMBOs that are relevant to the user active with that user's messages. There is no point in all PMBOs carrying messages for a user that only uses certain PMBOs.

A message sent from either another radio user or the Internet to a non-user will result in an automated message from the system stating that no such user is registered in the system. Users who do not check into the system for over six months are automatically purged from the system. Thereafter, they become a registered user again only when they once again check into the system.

USING *AIRMAIL*

AirMail is one of the great strengths of the Winlink 2000 (WL2K) system. Just like any other e-mail application, by using a sophisticated program at the user's station, a much more friendly and error-free interface is provided to the user, and many more features and services are supported than with the traditional teleprinter-style keyboard interface. As with any Internet e-mail program, composing messages before going

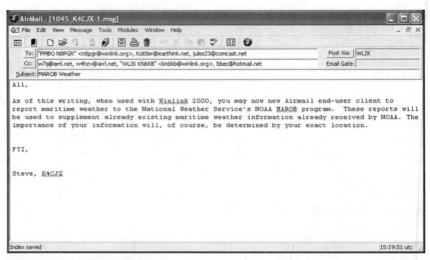

The *AirMail* message form.

"on-line" also reduces the connect time on an HF connection where the spectrum is so valuable, allowing more users to access a given PMBO than is possible in keyboard mode. Also, advanced formats may be implemented easier with the use of this sophisticated client program, allowing the same messages to be compressed for shorter transmission times as well as providing the ability to add binary attachments such as, *Microsoft Word*, *Excel*, pictures or graphic weather files. Using *AirMail* instead of a keyboard mode not only allows messages to be written off-line so that the shortest, most efficient time is spent on the radio transferring data, but also speeds of up to 3600 bits per second permit transmissions which are hundreds of times faster than composing messages in real-time while on the air.

There is a limited terminal mode for interactive keyboard commands, allowing a terminal rather than computer-based software to connect to a PMBO. This method discouraged, and is only used for listing and deletion of messages.

Today the end-user program of choice for HF radio is the *AirMail* client application written and supported by Jim Corenman, KE6RK. This is a very elegant user program that supports all of the features of WL2K and is provided for amateur use at no charge. It may be found on the Web at **www.airmail2000.com**.

USING *AIRMAIL* TO EMPLOY THE MANY FEATURES OF WINLINK 2000

AirMail is intended to employ many of the features of the existing Amateur Radio digital networks, and to link the additional features of Winlink 2000 that are of particular value to amateur users who do not have access to the Internet

With the *AirMail*'s end-user program, you can preset and control your radio if you configure it properly. Just choose a station, pick a frequency and push **SEND**. All information transfer is automatic and would be set up prior to the actual transmission just like any other e-mail agent. For the *AirMail* user, a continually updated list of PMBO stations and a built-in catalog update containing weather, as well as other helpful information, may both be requested via a radio download. Also, a continuously updated list may be found on the Web at **winlink.org/stations.htm** under "Winlink participating station (PMBO) center frequency list."

Remember that Winlink 2000 stations usually scan through several frequencies. If you can't connect, the Winlink 2000 station may already be busy with another user, or propagation conditions may not be favorable on the frequency you've chosen. Either try again later, or use the built-in propagation feature to connect on another band or to another Winlink participating station (PMBO). The number of frequencies scanned by the

An *AirMail* catalog.

PMBO you are calling determines the length of your call. An FEC identification burst containing the called station and your call will be sent at the end of your transmission even if you do not successfully connect to a PMBO. This is a legal requirement for all Amateurs using the system, regardless of their country of origin.

In addition to *AirMail*, the VHF/UHF client program, *Paclink* employs Microsoft's *Outlook* or *Outlook Express* as well as Eudora's e-mail agents as an interface to the short-haul VHF/UHF packet module for Winlink 2000. When used with Telpac, a network node relay, which uses Telnet to reach a PMBO, *Paclink* can be a powerful communications tool for local and regional UHF/VHF communications. This will be discussed separately.

TRANSPARENT INTERWORKING WITH INTERNET E-MAIL

The primarily purpose of WL2K is to assist the mobile or remotely located user. Because of this, WL2K supports a clean seamless transparent interface to the Internet SMTP (Simple Message Internet Protocol) e-mail system. Any message may include any number of Internet addresses, and a WL2K radio user may be addressed simply with his call @winlink.org. The call, however, must be known to the system as a radio user or the message will be rejected. This SMTP aspect has an added benefit in case of an emergency where local services are interrupted, allowing anyone familiar with Internet e-mail the ability to use the system.

What does all this mean to you? From the Internet side of Winlink 2000, friends and family can send e-mail to you just as they would send e-mail to anyone else on the Internet. In fact, the idea of Winlink 2000 is to make HF e-mail exchanges look essentially the same as regular Internet e-mail from the user's point of view. Internet users simply address their messages to **<your call sign>@winlink.org**. For example, a message addressed to **k4cjx@winlink.org** will be available to me when I check into any Winlink 2000 station (PMBO), but only if I was already properly registered as a Winlink 2000. This is accomplished by simply logging into any Winlink 2000 participating station (PMBO). Thereafter, checking into other PMBOs will bring your mail to them for pickup, also.

Through the *AirMail* end-user "client" software, the ham user can address messages to anyone over the Internet using the above format,

The Options message form.

or to other hams for that matter, simply by addressing the ham call sign only (i.e.: wb8imy) or **call sign@winlink.org**.

Most messages are routed as a standard e-mail message. Multiple carbon copies (cc) or blind carbon copies (bcc) may also be received from the Internet. This feature may be turned off by the user in the *AirMail* "Options Message" menu, which provides other user definable options for the end-user. Messages handled by WL2K may have any number of addressees labeled either "To:" or "Cc:" and may mix any combination of radio and Internet SMTP style addresses.

TRANSPARENT FILE ATTACHMENTS

Files of any type or number may be attached to a message by simply selecting the file to be sent from a *Windows* selection dialog in the user's *AirMail* program. Users receiving messages from WL2K may limit the size of file attachments (down to zero) they are willing to receive. The PACTOR protocol chosen by the user usually should dictate the file size of an attachment.

Remember that the radio link is very slow (especially compared to the Internet). Normally, sending an attachment of more than 80,000 bytes is not a good idea. Text, RTF, DOC, XLS, JPG, BMP, GIF, WMO, GREB and TIF files are permitted as long as they are small enough to comply with the particular user-set limit. The Winlink 2000 "B2F" binary format compresses files when possible. For example, a text-based file is compressed about 44 percent; a JPG file is compressed very little while a 400,000-byte BMP file may be compressed to as little as 15,000 bytes.

Speed (and file size) depends on the PACTOR protocol used. For example, PACTOR I provides a maximum of 200 Bits per second, PACTOR II provides a maximum of 800 bits per second while PACTOR III provides a maximum of over 3600 bits per second. In the real world, this means that an 80,000-byte text file typically takes 80 minutes to transfer over PACTOR I, 20 minutes over PACTOR 2, but *only 5 minutes over PACTOR III.*

SOPHISTICATED BULLETIN DISTRIBUTION

To address the needs of mobile users for near real-time data, WL2K uses an on-demand bulletin distribution mechanism. Users must first select requested bulletins from an available catalog managed in *AirMail*. When bulletin requests are received by a PMBO, a fresh locally cached copy of the requested bulletin is delivered. If no freshly local cached version is available, the PMBO accesses the Web and the bulletin is downloaded to the PMBO and then sent to the user. The catalog currently includes over 700 available weather, propagation, and information bulletins, including, instructions for using the system, world news and high-seas piracy reports. All WL2K PMBOs support a single global catalog, which insures user access to any bulletin from any PMBO. Bulletins can contain basic text, graphic fax or satellite images, binary or encoded files like GRIB or WMO weather reports. Local processing is used to reprocess images to sizes suitable for HF PACTOR transmission. The system prevents bulletin duplication and automatically purges obsolete time-sensitive weather bulletins and replaces them with the current version. WL2K also has the capability to accept limited packet BBS type bulletins received from other packet BBSs.

USER SELECTABLE PREFERENCES

Using *AirMail*'s Options Message form, an individual user may send automatic service messages to any WL2K PMBO that will establish user-definable preferences system-wide. Such options include the size of acceptable file attachments, an alternate e-mail or radio address for temporary message forwarding, Bcc messages coming from Internet as well as other options. The user simply brings up the form, fills in the desirable user-definable options and then pushes **Send** on the Options Message form. The next time a user checks into any PMBO, these options will be sent to the Winlink 2000 system and applied to his call.

POSITION REPORTS AND NOAA'S NWS MAROB REPORTING.

Another fascinating feature of Winlink 2000 is the ability to provide position reports for mobile users. Through the use of *AirMail*, they may be manually entered or sent electronically into *AirMail* from a hand-held GPS through the GPS NMEA port. There are four ways in which a family member or friend may query position reports and determine where you are (or at least where you were at the last report). The three methods, obtain a graphic position report of a mobile user on a series of maps. These are the Automatic Position Reporting System (APRS), YotReps, or ShipTrak, a map tracking facility offered by the Maritime Mobile Service Net.

Simply go to the Winlink 2000 home page menu at **www.winlink.org** and click on **Position Reporter**. Enter the Winlink user's call sign and you are shown various views, depending on which service you choose. With APRS, in US territories, you may also see a satellite photo of the site!

The fourth method, which can provide historical tracking of up to 30 days, is to send an e-mail message addressed to **qth@winlink.org** requesting the report. The subject line of the message must be **Position Request**. The body of the message contains the call signs of interest (one call sign per line.) Once this request has been sent, a response with the requested information will be received as normal text e-mail.

The National Weather Service's NOAA MAROB weather reporting facility has is also contained on the *AirMail* client software position reporting form for maritime users. This facility provides an opportunity for maritime users to report maritime weather conditions to NOAA. A special weather category is being employed which will contain all such valid reports in an attempt to fill in the blanks where other weather reporting is weak or non-existent. More about MAROB weather may be obtained on the Web at **www.nws.noaa.gov/om/marine/marob.htm**.

The position and weather reporting capabilities within Winlink 2000 aides immeasurably to the safety and well-being of those using the

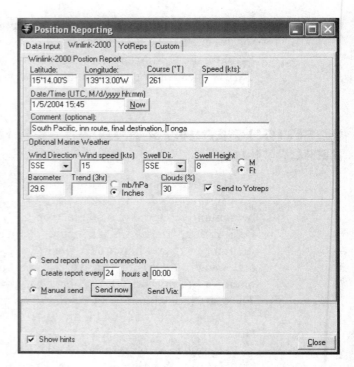

An *AirMail* Position Reporting/NWS NOAA MAROB form.

Winlink 2000 system as well as for those who are concerned about their family and friends who are Winlink 2000 users.

PROPAGATION ASSISTANCE

AirMail uses the *ICEPAC* propagation program as a prediction engine. In order to use *AirMail*'s propagation window, I*CEPAC* must be downloaded and installed into its own default directory. Once installed, the program works as a part of *AirMail* to provide accurate propagation information to assist the Winlink 2000 user in determining which participating stations (PMBOs) are available for connection. Each time a user connects to a PMBO, the current Solar Flux Index is automatically passed to the *AirMail* client using the *ICEPAC* propagation module. This, of course, adds greatly to the accuracy of the prediction information.

An *AirMail* Propagation form.

FULL ACCESS TO RADIO MESSAGES WITH THE *AIRMAIL* TELNET FEATURE

AirMail provides a high-speed replica of all WL2K radio operations while directly connected through the Internet to one of the participating network station (PMBO) telnet servers. This method of obtaining messages over the Internet allows attachments, catalog bulletins and all other Winlink 2000 services normally available over radio channels, but at much faster normal Internet speeds. One must be a registered radio user to access the *AirMail* telnet feature.

LIMITED ACCESS TO RADIO MESSAGES WITH A WEB BROWSER

There are times when radio users may need to send or receive messages when separated from their radio access or *AirMail* system. This may be done with password protected Web access from any Web browser. Messages sent and received by this method are limited to text-based messages and without the use of bulletins or file attachments. In order to use this service, a user must have logged in over radio within the last 6 months. Again, to become a registered and legally verified radio user, all one must do is log in over the air to one of the existing PMBOs at least every 6 months.

SYSTEM WIDE USER NOTICES

The WL2K network administrator may post system wide notices that are delivered to all individual WL2K users as a private message. This is a valuable tool for notifying users of system enhancements, outages, software upgrades or emergencies.

SUPPORT FOR AN OPTIMAL NUMBER OF PARTICIPATING WINLINK PMBOS

The WL2K system will support an optimal number of individual participating PMBOs in order to cover the global traffic volumes. Requirements for becoming a PMBO may be obtained by contacting the WL2K system administrator, K4CJX, at **k4cjx@comcast.net**. For those who are not interested in becoming a full-time PMBO, the VHF/UHF Telpac option may be in order. Telpac information and download may be found on the Web at **www.winlink.org/features.htm**.

USER TIME LIMITS

To ensure equitable access to the system individual users are assigned daily time limits on HF frequencies by PMBO sysops. The default time per any 24 hour period is 30 minutes, however, the user may request more time from the PMBO sysop should it be needed. Remember, the time limit is individual to each PMBO station. Utilization of the PACTOR II and PACTOR III protocols are a great timesaver, allowing the user up to 18 times the volume of messages over that of PACTOR I for the same period of time.

OTHER FEATURES

The system has a number of other secondary features to help keep it healthy. Extensive traffic reports are collected, the state of individual PMBO and the CMBO are monitored (**winlink.org/status**), and daily backups are performed automatically at all PMBOs as well as the two redundant Central Servers (CMBO) to insure the system integrity. Security is insured through the vigorous updating of virus definitions and automatic virus screening for all Internet mail and files. The system has the ability to block any user by both radio (by frequency band) and Internet (by e-mail address) to prevent abuse of the system. Spam is controlled using several services that control spam e-mail.

USER DRIVEN SYSTEM

The Winlink 2000 system was developed from a long list of user requirements. With obvious focus on the individual user groups, the Winlink development team continually seeks feature ideas and system concepts from the user community it serves. If you are interested in digital radio, there is a place for you and your ideas with Winlink 2000.

As a result of providing the Amateur Radio community with an ever-expanding system, the Winlink development team has enhanced the ability of Winlink 2000 to deal with emergency communications. Much information regarding this subject may be found on the Winlink 2000 Web site at **winlink.org/emergency.htm**.

THE WINLINK 2000 VHF/UHF TELPAC MODULE FOR EXPANDED LOCAL PACKET RADIO ACCESS

Mainly designed to satisfy the requirements and requests of the Amateur ARES/RACES community, the Winlink development team has added two new modules to its client (user based) applications for delivering mail from the Winlink 2000 system to the wireless ham user. "Telpac" stands for TELnet PACket Bridge. Telpac is optimized to easily interface Winlink 2000 to conventional VHF/UHF Packet users and BBSs. This includes simple portable terminals (e.g. Palm devices), as well as more capable FBB compatible programs including *AirMail* packet.

Telpac efficiently links conventional amateur AX.25 packet to Winlink 2000 's Telnet Servers and uses the *AGW Packet Engine*, which supports virtually all Packet TNCs (including BayCom and sound cards). TNCs can be remote and shared with other *AGW Packet Engine* applications. Telpac is simple to set up and run and requires a minimum of computer and radio equipment. The Telpac software runs independently from the more complex Winlink 2000 Network PMBO software. Telpac is ideal for a temporary emergency management setup or any other unattended remote location where it can deliver reliable wireless communication to the last mile.

Telpac takes VHF/UHF AX.25 packet, adds the ability to add binary attachments with the B2F protocol and automatically links with the Winlink 2000 network via Telnet to a participating Winlink network station (PMBO.) As of this writing, future plans include using HF linking as an emergency alternative to the existing telnet link.

Paclink is the client (user) based module that talks to the Telpac node. It employs *Microsoft's Outlook* or *Outlook Express* and operates seamlessly in an Internal LAN network as just another mail server. *Paclink* employs the *AGW Packet Engine* for ease of use with just about any generation of packet TNC or even a sound card. *Paclink* also has a telnet option to VHF/UHF packet. *Paclink* is a relatively small program and will operate on *Windows 2000 Professional, XP Home* or *Pro* editions. *Paclink* uses the new Microsoft .NET framework.

More about Telpac and *Paclink* may be found at **www.winlink.org/Client.htm# - Te-Pac**.

THE FUTURE OF WINLINK 2000

In today's hamming environment, digital message transfer is relatively new, but growing rapidly. It has many uses that are relevant to our hobby. First of all, it shows those who are skeptical about the ability of the ham community that we are still on the cutting edge of technology. Secondly, it is helping to boost services such as Emergency Management (**winlink.org/emergency.htm**). As long as Winlink 2000 continues to embrace enabling technologies, it will continue to grow and attract those who have an interest in computing, radio, Emergency Management and other similar disciplines. The amateur priorities of the past are not necessarily those of the future, and those developing the feature sets and structure of Winlink 2000 are aware that of these facts.

As of this writing, the Winlink development team is planning for Winlink 2004 that will expand the service it employs to an even greater audience of Amateur radio users. A prime example of this is the inclusion of Telpac and *Paclink* into the existing structure.

HOW TO GET INVOLVED

If you have an interest in Winlink 2000, you may wish to periodically review the Winlink Web site, **www.winlink.org**, for further developments as it simplifies the requirements for a participating on many levels. In summary, those involved with the development of this technology welcome newcomers with open arms. It may just a fun and desirably effective tool for your own use. You never know until you investigate its many uses.

Chapter SEVEN

CLOVER

According to legend, the late Ray Petit, W7GHM, was working on a revolutionary new HF digital communication system in his home lab. His wife stopped by just in time to see a display of the received signal pattern on Ray's oscilloscope. "That looks just like a Clover," she remarked. The new mode didn't have a name and his wife's description seemed appropriate enough. Why not simply call it *Clover*?

WHAT IS CLOVER?

Clover is an advanced HF digital communication system which Ray developed in a joint venture with HAL Communications of Urbana, Illinois. Clover uses a four-tone modulation scheme. An enhanced version using improved DSP technology came along later and was officially christened Clover 2000, but I'll refer to the mode simply as "Clover" throughout this chapter for the sake of clarity.

Depending on signal conditions, several different modulation formats can be selected manually or automatically. Each tone is phase- and/or amplitude-modulated as a separate, narrow-bandwidth data channel. As you might guess, the resulting Clover signal is very complex!

For example, when the tone pulses are modulated using quadrature phase-shift modulation (QPSM), the differential phase of each tone shifts in 90° increments. Two bits of data are carried by each tone for a total of eight bits in each 32-ms frame. The resulting block data rate is about 250 bits per second. Clover is capable of even higher data rates when using 16-phase, four-amplitude modulation (16P4A). In this format, Clover perks along at 750 bit/s.

The complex, higher-speed modulation systems are used when conditions are favorable. When the going gets rough, Clover automatically brings several slower (but more robust) modes into play.

Even with these ingenious adaptive modulation systems, errors are bound to occur. That's where Clover's Reed-Solomon coding fills the gaps. Reed-Solomon coding is used in all Clover modes. Errors are detected at the receiving station by comparing check bytes that are inserted in each block of transmitted text. When operating in the ARQ (automatic repeat request) mode, Clover's damaged data can often be reconstructed without the need to request repeat transmissions (sort of a nonARQ type of ARQ!). This is a major departure from the techniques used by PACTOR. Of course, Clover can't always repair data; repeat transmissions—which Clover handles automatically—are sometimes required to get everything right.

With the combination of adaptive modulation systems and Reed-Solomon coding, Clover boasts remarkable performance—even under the worst HF conditions. The only Amateur Radio digital mode with the

The Clover Waveform

The Clover waveform consists of four tone pulses, each of which is 125-Hz wide, spaced at 125-Hz centers. The four tone pulses are sequential, with only one tone being present at any instant and each tone lasting 8 ms. Each frame consists of four tone pulses lasting a total of 32 ms, so the base modulation rate of a Clover signal is always 31.25 symbols per second. Data is conveyed by changing the phase and/or amplitude of successive pulses at the same frequency. These changes are made only at the instant midway between the peaks of two successive pulses when their amplitudes are zero. The measured Clover modulation spectra is tightly confined within a 500 Hz bandwidth, with outside edges sup-pressed 50 dB to prevent interference to adjacent frequencies. Unlike other modulation schemes, the Clover modulation spectra is the same for all modulation formats. Additional key parameters of Clover modulation include a symbol rate of 31.25 symbol/s (regardless of the type of modulation being used), 2:1 voltage (6 dB power) crest factor, and an ITU-R emission designator of 500H J2 DEN or 500H J2 BEN.

potential to match Clover's performance is PACTOR II, and possibly G-TOR (under certain conditions).

CLOVER HANDSHAKING

As you may recall, PACTOR uses an *over* command to switch the link so that one station can send while the other receives. Clover links must be switched as well, but the switching takes place *without* using *over* commands.

When two Clover stations make contact, they can send limited amounts of data to each other (up to 30 characters in each block) in what is known as the *chat mode*. If the amount of data waiting for transmission at one station exceeds 30 characters, Clover automatically switches to the *block data mode*. The transmitted blocks immediately become larger and are sent much faster. The other station, however, remains in the chat mode. Because of precise frame timing, all of this takes place without the need for either operator to change settings, or send *over* commands. The Clover controllers at both stations "know" when to switch from transmit to receive and vice versa. And what if both stations have large amounts of data to send at the same time? Then they *both* switch to the data block mode. This high degree of efficiency is transparent to you, the operator.

The four-tone Clover waveform compared to HF packet and AMTOR waveforms.

All you have to do is type your comments or select the file you want to send—Clover takes care of everything else!

Clover features an FEC mode similar to that used by PACTOR and G-TOR. You use the Clover FEC to call CQ, or to send transmissions that can be received by several stations at once. (In the Clover ARQ mode, only two stations can communicate at a time.)

WHAT DO I NEED TO RUN CLOVER?

The requirements for a Clover station differ somewhat from those of other HF digital modes. They are:

• An SSB transceiver. The transceiver must be stable (less than 30 Hz drift per hour). It should also include a frequency display with 10-Hz

The Reed-Solomon Error Detection and Correction Algorithm

Reed-Solomon FEC is used in all Clover modes. This is a powerful byte and block oriented error-correction technique, not available in other common HF data modes, and it can allow the receiving station to correct errors without requiring a repeat transmission. Errors are detected on octets of data rather than on the individual bits themselves. This error correction technique is ideally suited for HF use in which errors due to fades or interferences are often "bursty" (short-lived) but cause total destruction of a number of sequential data bits. Error correction at the receiver is determined by "check" bytes which are inserted in each block by the transmitter. The receiver uses these check bytes to reconstruct data which has been damaged during transmission. The capacity of the error corrector to fix errors is limited and set by how many check bytes are sent per block. Check bytes are also "overhead" on the signal and their addition effectively reduces the efficiency and therefore the "throughput rate" at which user data is passed between transmitter and receiver. Efficiencies of 60%, 75% or 90% can be invoked by using successively lower levels of Reed-Solomon encoding for error correction, or 100% efficiency by bypassing this algorithm. Better propagation conditions do not require as much error correction, which means the amount of overhead decreases and the efficiency increases.

How CLOVER Works

By Ray Petit, W7GHM (SK)

To adequately explain why CLOVER is such a breakthrough, we must first briefly review the pluses and minuses of existing HF data modes—RTTY, AMTOR, and HF packet radio.

RTTY of course led the way for automatic reception of characters or data via HF radio. RTTY has been around since the 1940s and is very reliable. The techniques we use today to send and receive RTTY are much the same as those first used. We have better equipment, but use the same FSK modulation and Baudot or ASCII code. RTTY is slow and does not offer any error correction or detection. RTTY speeds of 60 WPM (45 baud) to 100 WPM (75 baud) are common. Increasing the RTTY spreads increases the errors; we generally stick to 45 baud.

AMTOR evolved from an existing ship-to-shore "radio telex" mode, often called "TOR" or "SITOR" (CCIR 4767 and CCIR 625). AMTOR introduced us to a new type of data link — "ARQ mode" (ARQ stands for Automatic Repeat Request).

AMTOR characters are coded so that the receiving station can detect an error in each character sent. The sending station sends three characters, turns the transmitter OFF, and listens for a character response from the receiving station. The response is either "all OK, send next three," or "repeat last three characters." Like RTTY, it is also pretty "slow." Under the best conditions, AMTOR can pass data at an equivalent RTTY rate of 50 baud (6.67 characters per second). AMTOR is also limited to the same character set as Baudot — just all capital letters and no ASCII control characters.

CLOVER intends to support the many advantages of AMTOR and HF packet radio and fixes the major problems of these modes. The most serious limitation of RTTY, AMTOR, and HF packet is data throughput and how the data is used to modulate the radio signal. The ionosphere is not a friendly medium for data signals. HF signals often arrive at the receiving antenna by many different propagation paths; two or more paths are common. Each signal path has its own time delay, amplitude, and even different center frequency. The receiving antenna does not discriminate; it adds all the signals and passes the composite to the receiver. The amplitudes and phases of the separate ac signals combine algebraically to produce a widely varying receiver input. Deep selective fades and time smearing of the data pulse transitions are the usual result.

Once combined at the antenna, the individual path signals are not easily separated. It is usually impossible to compensate for all of these "multipath" effects in the demodulator. A good example of multipath ionosphere distortion is the "selective fading" we hear when listening to music from a shortwave radio station. While annoying when listening to music, the distortion can be totally destructive to data transmissions.

A major nonrecoverable parameter of HF data is the time at which the data state changes from MARK to SPACE, the data transition time. If we lose this information, the modem can no longer tell when one data pulse ends and the next one begins or if the logic state should be a "1" or a "0." When two signals arrive with different propagation time delays, the composite antenna output signal is "smeared" and the transition times overlap. Measurements by Ray and many others show that we can expect this time overlap from different paths to be as much as 3 to 5 milliseconds (ms). At least one half of each data pulse without distortion determines the MARK or SPACE data state. Therefore, the narrowest data pulse which can be reliably demodulated is on the order of 6 to 10 ms, corresponding to maximum data rates in the range of 100 to 167 baud. Observation shows that the 100-baud limit is more realistic and even it can be too high for satisfactory data transmission at times.

HF packet radio uses a 300-baud data rate, a pulse width of 3.3 milliseconds. Successful HF packet transmissions are therefore very unlikely if the signal is propagated by multiple paths. HF packet works well only when the operating frequency is close to the Maximum Usable Frequency (MUF)—when there is only one propagation path. Since this is the exception and not the rule, long-term packet performance on a single fixed frequency is pretty poor, and many repeats may be required to pass any data at all.

HF packet radio, AMTOR, and RTTY all use FSK modulation. One radio frequency is sent for the "1" or MARK pulse state and another for the "0" or SPACE state. The transmitter carrier frequency is shifted back and forth at the same rate as the data. CLOVER uses different modulation techniques. First, CLOVER shifts the phase and not the frequency of the carrier. Second, more than one bit of data can be sent per phase state. For example, BPSK (binary phase shift keying) has two phase states (0 or 180 degrees) which can be used to represent MARK and SPACE. QPSK (Quadrature PSK) has four phase states (0, 90, 180, 270 degrees). A single-phase change in QPSK represents the state of two binary bits of data. Similarly, 8PSK can send the state of 3 bits per phase change and 16PSK can send 4 bits per phase change.

CLOVER also allows use of Amplitude Shift Keying (ASK) in the 8PSK and 16PSK modes. We call these modes "8P2A" (4 data bits per phase/amplitude change) and "16P4A" (6 bits per phase/amplitude change.) Since all changes in phase or amplitude occur at the fixed base rate of 31.25 BPS (an equivalent pulse width of 32 ms), data errors due to multipath time smearing of data transitions are minimized.

The CLOVER modulation strategy is to always send data at a very slow base modulation rate and to use multi-level changes in phase or amplitude to speed up data flow. One final twist to CLOVER-II is that there are four separate transmitted pulses, each separated by 125 Hz.

Each of the pulses may be modulated by BPSK through 16PSK plus 8P2A or 16P4A modulation. This further multiplies that effective throughput by a factor of four. Putting it all together, CLOVER can send data at rates from its base data rate (31.25 bps) to 24 times its base rate (750 bps). Wow! It's almost like getting something for nothing! Not quite so. There are still problems to be solved.

PSK modulation itself poses some pretty serious problems. IF we modulate a continuous carrier using PSK, the frequency spectrum we get is very bad for HF use, as sidebands are strong and extend over a wide spectrum. CLOVER avoids this problem by two techniques:

(1) Each of the four tones is an ON/OFF amplitude pulse and the phase is changed only when the pulse is OFF;

(2) The amplitude waveform of each ON/OFF pulse is carefully shaped to minimize the resulting frequency spectrum.

Combined, these techniques produce a composite CLOVER spectrum that is only 500 Hz wide down to −60 dB. This is one half the radio bandwidth required for AMTOR and one quarter that for HF packet radio at an effective data rate of up to 100 times faster than HF packet radio or AMTOR!

CLOVER also takes a different approach to error correction. AMTOR and packet radio both correct errors by sensing errors at the receiver and then requesting repeat transmissions. When there are errors to be fixed, data throughput is slowed by the time it takes to send the repeats. When conditions are getting poor, packet radio bogs down to sending only repeats and no data at all; AMTOR will slow down considerably under the same conditions.

CLOVER uses a Reed-Solomon error correction code that allows the receiver to actually fix errors WITHOUT requiring repeat transmissions.

For a moderate number of errors, CLOVER doesn't require repeats and the data continuous flowing at the no-error rate. To distinguish between the two schemes, we classify AMTOR and packet radio as "error-detection" protocols and CLOVER as an "error-correction" protocol. In addition, like packet radio, CLOVER includes a CRC (Cyclic Redundancy Check sum) which is used when conditions are very bad and the number of errors exceeds the capacity of the Reed-Solomon error corrector.

CLOVER ARQ mode is also adaptive. As a result of the DSP calculations necessary to detect multi-level PSK and ASK, the CLOVER receiver already has information which can be used to determine the signal-to-noise ratio (S/N), phase dispersion, and time dispersion of the received signal. CLOVER has 8 different modulation modes, 4 different error correction settings, and 4 different data block lengths that can be used— a total of 128 different modulation/code/block combinations!

Using real-time signal analysis, the CLOVER receiver will automatically signal the transmitting state to change modes to match existing ionosphere conditions. When propagation is very good, CLOVER can set itself to the higher speed and data literally "screams" down the path.

When conditions are not so great, the data speed is slowed. As noted earlier, the CLOVER character throughput rate under typical HF conditions is about ten times faster than AMTOR or HF packet, However when we get one of those perfect conditions, CLOVER will "shift gears" and pass data at 50 to 100 times the speed of AMTOR of HF packet radio. In all cases, CLOVER automatically changes speeds to give the maximum speed that the ionosphere will allow.

resolution. The audio output from the Clover controller is fed to the audio input of the transceiver (Clover uses AFSK, not FSK). Receive audio is supplied to the controller from the external speaker jack or other source.

• An IBM-PC computer or compatible. The computer must be at least a 286-level machine.

• A P-38 Clover controller board or a DXP38 HF modem (see Chapter 2). All Clover products are available exclusively from HAL Communications (see the Resource Guide for details). The HAL P-38 Clover controller is installed *inside* the computer using any available expansion slot. The board uses a dual-microprocessor design and digital signal processing to achieve signal modulation and demodulation. The DXP38 HF modem, on the other hand, is an external device.

Clover-II Specifications for the HAL P-38 and DXP38 Processors

Format: 4-tone emission
Bandwidth: 500 Hz @ −50 dB
ARQ Mode Modulation: BPSM, QPSM, and 8PSM
FEC Mode Modulation: 2DPSM, BPSM, QPSM, and 8PSM
Tones: 2250 Hz Center
Symbol Rate: 31.25 per second
Error Correction Coding: Reed-Solomon code: 60, 75 or 90%
  code rate
ARQ Protocol: 2-level, multiblock auto adaptive modulation
Adaptive Mode Control: Measure S/N & Phase on all data, set
  TX Mode
ARQ Thru-put: 8 to 35 bytes/second
FEC Thru-put: 4 to 25 bytes/second
FSK RTTY Codes: Baudot and ASCII
ASCII Codes: 45, 50, 57, 75 baud
RTTY Tones: 1275/1445 or 2125/2295 Hz
AMTOR Code: CCIR-476 & CCIR-625
AMTOR Modes: ARQ or FEC
AMTOR Tones: 1275/1445 or 2125/2295 Hz
AMTOR Rate: 100 baud
PACTOR Modes: Auto-ARQ & FEC
PACTOR Rates: 100/200 baud

• HAL PC-Clover software. This is supplied by HAL Communications and is included with every P-38 and DXP38. It is *not* a terminal program. The PC-Clover software is the instruction set of the controller itself! It's loaded into the controller's memory each time you decide to operate. This approach makes it easy to update the controller in the future. You simply buy a new diskette or download the software. There are also third-party programs that will function with either product.

The original Clover controllers cost approximately $1,000. In the late '90s HAL introduced the P-38 with a selling price of less than $400. Then, in early 1999, the external DXP38 appeared, also selling at under $400. Both products are multimode processors. That is, they offer RTTY, AMTOR, PACTOR (HAL refers to it as "P-Mode") and Clover.

CLOVER ON THE AIR

Most Clover-equipped stations are dedicated to relaying high-volume message traffic, often functioning as HF/Internet e-mail gateways. This makes casual Clover operating the exception rather than the rule, although you will find occasional keyboard-to-keyboard "live" chats.

Clover signals are relatively easy to recognize. The data bursts vary in length. Some are short, while others can last several seconds. The signals make a staccato *brrrrrr* sound rather than the chirping rhythms of PACTOR and G-TOR.

Clover Conversations

When it comes to on-the-air operating, Clover is different from any of the modes we've discussed so far. To call CQ, for example, you switch to the **MODE** menu, highlight **CQ** and press **ENTER**. The Clover controller sends a CW identification followed by a raucous stream of data. Unlike other digital modes, you do not see "CQ CQ CQ" flowing across your screen. In fact, you see nothing at all.

The controller sends CQ in the form of data signals that appear as CQ "flags" to other Clover stations. When another Clover operator tunes in your signal, all he sees is a statement on his screen announcing that you are calling CQ. At that point he can ignore you or press a single key to establish a Clover connection.

Once the conversation has started, you need to let the other station know when you've completed a statement. Remember that there are no *over* commands. For example:

QST Reviews the HAL Communications DXP38

(from April 2000 *QST*)

The HAL DXP38 does not offer as many modes as other MCPs, but it does extremely well with what it *does* offer: PACTOR, RTTY, ASCII, AMTOR and CLOVER II. The DXP38 manual is the best of the group. It is well written, well organized and concise. The writing style is conversational with a slight touch of humor. You hardly need the manual to install the DXP38. Unlike the other MCPs in this group, the DXP38 uses RCA phono jacks on the rear panel, which makes cabling a breeze. (If you've ever soldered several wires onto a DIN plug, you know what we mean.)

Once you're up and running, you have your choice of FSK for RTTY, AMTOR and PACTOR, or AFSK for the entire set. Clover II must be sent using AFSK, so we opted for AFSK for all of our testing. A trim pot to adjust the transmit audio level is accessible from the rear panel. HAL Communications has a long history in HF digital communication. Its RTTY terminal units are still considered among the best in the world. It's no surprise, then, that the RTTY performance of the DXP38 was the best in the group. In weak-signal conditions and brutal contest environments, the DXP38 consistently copied RTTY when the other MCPs displayed mostly gibberish.

The hardware tuning indicator—an LED emulation of the traditional "crossed bananas" oscilloscope display—was a joy to use. Even weak, interference-laden signals could be tuned quickly and accurately. The DXP38's PACTOR performance (HAL refers to this as *P-Mode*) was also outstanding. We were able to establish and hold PACTOR links under marginal conditions. Only the SCS PTC-IIe could top the DXP38 in this category.

We ran into difficulty testing the DXP38 on AMTOR, but that had nothing to do with the device itself. AMTOR signals are as rare as proverbial hen's teeth these days and the only way we could conduct AMTOR tests with this or any of the other MCPs was to arrange skeds. Despite the hassles, the DXP38 seemed to acquit itself very well in this mode. And then there is Clover II. This complicated 4-tone mode is the chief competitor to SCS's

PACTOR II. Both modes have been doing battle for dominance in the commercial and amateur markets for years. Of course, both companies insist that their mode is superior and can present evidence to prove their cases. In our brief, informal tests... it was a draw. We did not notice substantial performance differences between PACTOR II and Clover II. Under identical conditions both modes appeared to transfer our sample files in roughly the same amounts of time.

As with PACTOR II, the overall performance of Clover II was remarkable, maintaining links and transferring data in conditions under which we could just barely hear the other stations. Clover requires high transceiver stability (± 5 Hz drift per hour, maximum) and slow, careful tuning for optimal results. The DXP38's tuning indicator was helpful, but it is only updated every 2 seconds in Clover II, so you have to tune very carefully. Once you find a Clover signal (it sounds like an extended *brrrrrr*) and tune it in, the best thing to do is leave your radio alone. Even a slight VFO tweak is sufficient to break the link. HAL Communications was the only company to provide both *DOS* and *Windows* software with their product. We used the *Windows* software and it worked extremely well. (Some preferred the *Windows* tuning indicator for Clover II rather than the hardware display.) Unlike the other burst modes, Clover II is bi-directional, which means that it is sending and receiving information at regular intervals without waiting for an "over" command from the operator. This made live QSOs a bit tricky because the one operator could begin commenting on something you said before you were even finished saying it! Despite the excellent performance of Clover II, hams have not embraced this mode in large numbers. The fact that the Winlink 2000 e-mail network is almost exclusively based on PACTOR will not help this situation in the immediate future. Clover BBSs and live QSOs are not as scarce as G-TOR or AMTOR contacts, but they are not plentiful, either.

**Hello! My name is Steve
and I live in Wallingford, Connecticut. I am new to
Clover. What do you think of it? >>>**

Without >>>, BTU, K or a similar symbol at the end of my statement, the other operator might inadvertently jump in after the end of the first line. This can be very confusing for everyone!

While you're watching the conversation, it's easy to get distracted by the receive/transmit status table in the upper right corner of the screen (if you're using the HAL software). The table displays the modulation format in use at the moment, the signal-to-noise ratio, tuning error, phase dispersion, error-correction capacity and transmitter output power (as a percentage of full output). The table is split into horizontal rows labeled "MY" and "HIS." Not only do you see your own parameters changing, you see the changes taking place *at the other station*! (Clover accomplishes this feat by periodically swapping station data.) Who is enjoying the best receive conditions? Which station is doing the greatest amount of error correcting at the moment? Just look at the table!

CLOVER BANDWIDTH

As we've already discussed, space is a premium in the HF digital subbands. That's why it's important for any HF digital mode to be as *narrow* as possible.

With a 2-kHz bandwidth, an HF packet signal is nearly as wide as a voice transmission. You can't squeeze too many packet signals onto the band before serious interference begins (just listen to the HF packet activity on 20 meters!).

As remarkable as it may seem, Clover manages to conduct extremely efficient communications while using only 500 Hz of spectrum! *Four* Clover signals could fit in the same amount of spectrum required for a one HF packet signal.

This narrow bandwidth is yet another prominent feature of Clover. Of course, a narrow-bandwidth signal requires more careful tuning. You can also understand why your transceiver must be very stable to operate Clover. With a 500-Hz wide signal, all it takes is a little bit of drift and you're way out of the ballpark!

Chapter EIGHT

Hellschreiber

Are the Hellschreiber modes really digital? Or, are they a hybrid of the analog and digital worlds?

Some argue that the Hellschreiber modes are more closely related to facsimile since they display text on your computer screen in the form of images (not unlike the product of a fax machine). On the other hand, the elements of the Hellschreiber "image text" are transmitting using a strictly defined digital format rather than the various analog signals of true HF fax or SSTV.

The Hellschreiber concept itself is quite old, developed in the 1920s by Rudolf Hell. Hellschreiber was, in fact, the first successful direct printing text transmission system. The German Army used Hellschreiber for field communications in World War II and the mode was in use for commercial landline service until about 1980.

As personal computers became ubiquitous tools in ham shacks throughout the world, interest in Hellschreiber as an HF mode increased. By the end of the 20th century amateurs had developed several sophisticated pieces of Hellschreiber software, and had expanded, and improved, the Hellschreiber system itself. All amateur Hellschreiber operating is done using sound-card software. So, the same sound-card station you may have assembled for modes such as PSK31 and RTTY can be used for Hellschreiber. It's just a matter of running a different program, or switching to the Hell mode in a multimode program (see the Resources chapter).

HOW DOES IT WORK?

Hell text is "painted" to the screen as the Hell tone is received. To receive a Hell signal, the computer program sets up the sound card to use DSP techniques for detecting the signal and places the output on a short vertically scanning line that is moving horizontally across the screen. This produces a single line of text in a marquee fashion that is wrapped around to eventually create a full screen of text.

The computer does not decode the Hellschreiber characters—that's a task left to your eyes and brain. The weakest link in decoding Hell characters will be your ability to distinguish letters under noisy conditions. Each Hell character is sent on a double line, so that if one character is difficult to read, or is shifted off the marquee, the other may still be visible. The result looks unusual, but it is readable under very poor conditions.

To send Hell characters, the computer program uses the sound card to modulate the transmitter in the same way that other sound card modes are transmitted. For Feld Hell, it is an on/off single tone, the same used for modulated CW. A properly adjusted Feld Hell input level will produce a bandwidth of no more than 75 Hz.

Like RTTY and PSK31, the Hellschreiber modes are intended for live conversations. Most of the activity is found on 20 meters, typically between 14077 and 14082 kHz, and between 14063 and 14065 kHz. There are many versions of Hell, although only a few see regular use.

Feld-Hell

Feld-Hell is the most popular Hellschreiber mode among HF digital experimenters. It has its roots in the original Hellschreiber format, adapted slightly for ham use. Feld-Hell is the mode you are most likely to encounter on the air.

Each character of a Feld-Hell transmission is communicated as a series of dots, with the result looking a bit like the output from a dot-matrix printer. A key-down state is used to indicate the black area of text

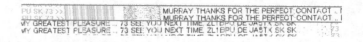

Murray, ZL1BPU, working a Japanese station on Feld-Hell over a 10,000 km path.

EA2BAJ running 16-tone concurrent MT-Hell.

and the key up state is used to indicate blank or white spaces. One hundred and fifty characters are transmitted every minute. Each character takes 400 ms to complete. Because there are 49 pixels per character, each pixel is 8.163 ms long.

Feld-Hell characters can be sent by using a simple CW transmitter, but most operators prefer to achieve the same effect by feeding 900 or 980-Hz tones an SSB transmitter. Whichever method is used, the timing requirements are precise. Fortunately, Rudolf Hell developed a simple technique of printing the text twice to deal with the effects of phase shifts and small timing errors. (The text is not transmitted twice, however.) In this sense you could say that Feld-Hell is a quasi-synchronous mode. The font was designed so that the top and bottom of each line of text could be matched, if necessary, to create readable words, no matter what phase relationship existed between transmitting and receiving equipment.

GL-Hell

The GL-Hell system uses the same 7 × 7 font field as Feld-Hell, but the characters in the font are modified by the addition of a "bar" up the left side, which acts as a "start bit" because this is an asynchronous system. Operation is at 300 baud and either 1000 or 3000 Hz keyed tones are used. Some European amateurs experiment with GL-Hell on VHF, but otherwise there is little activity.

PC-Hell

Over the years, various amateurs have experimented with asynchronous Hell transmissions that were compatible with existing RTTY equipment. This technique used the UART chip in early personal computers to transmit asynchronous characters for each character column. Even at 100 baud (as fast as most RTTY equipment would go), the text throughput using a simple 7 × 5 font with one stop bit was under two characters/second. It is almost never heard on the air today.

PSK-Hell and FM-Hell

PSK-Hell was invented in 1999 by Murray Greenman, ZL1BPU, and implemented by Nino Porcino, IZ8BLY. FM-Hell, developed by Nino IZ8BLY is technically similar, but with only one sideband. These modes have very impressive characteristics—very sensitive, rather like PSK-31, but unaffected by polar Doppler flutter and fading. They recover very quickly from lightning pulses due to the huge dynamic range and insensitivity to amplitude variations. FM-Hell suffers less from blurriness and text can look very sharp on poor paths.

PSK-Hell and FM-Hell are in fact *Differential* Phase Shift Keyed modes. PSK-Hell, like PSK-31, has the idle state signaled by a string of 180° phase changes at the baud rate, with raised cosine envelope, but there the similarity ends. FM-Hell combines frequency shift with phase shift to achieve a clean very narrow MSK-like single sideband transmission with no raised cosine modulation.

These modes transmit text in either a special low resolution 7 × 6 dot matrix at 105 baud, or a high resolution 14 × 7 dot matrix *Windows* font at 245 baud, so the character throughput and column rate are identical to Feld-Hell. A special font is required at 105 baud, in order to control the number of phase reversals in each character. It is not possible to use Rudolf Hell's resolution enhancing "two pixel rule" with 7 vertical pixels, so 245-baud mode is used. Black dots are sent by *not* reversing the phase at the beginning of the dot. The receiving process for both PSK-Hell and FM-Hell compares the phase of each dot with that of the previous dot. With 4× oversampling, Doppler phase errors are averaged out by the viewer. No clock recovery is required, as the system is an analog one, and quasi-synchronous like Feld-Hell.

FSK-Hell

Various software packages offer FSK versions of Feld-Hell. There

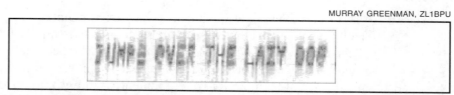

A test transmission on 80 meters between ZL1AN and ZL1BPU using 7-tone sequential MT-Hell.

appears to be no particular standard, although perhaps the IZ8BLY 245-Hz shift version is the most widespread. This version transmits 980 Hz for black, 1225 Hz for white surrounding the character, and silence for inter-character white, with an option for full-time white.

Duplo-Hell

This is a mode invented by Nino, IZ8BLY. The font and format are identical to Feld-Hell, except that two columns are transmitted at the same time, using two on-off keyed tones. These tones (980 Hz and 1225 or 1470 Hz for 245 or 490 Hz shift) can obviously be sent at the same time. The lower tone is used for the left column, and the upper for the right. Rather than operate at double throughput, the transmission runs at the same throughput as Feld-Hell (2.5 characters/sec), with the dot elements doubled in length.

This mode is remarkably immune to noise, due to the higher integration time for each dot element. The wider shift is more immune, but more sensitive to selective fading, which causes a "Venetian blind" effect.

Concurrent Multi-Tone Hell

With C/MT-Hell all rows of each character are transmitted at the same time using different tones, hence it is possible to send a truly vertical line. High resolution is possible allowing elaborate fonts to be used. The system is very interference immune.

Sequential Multi-Tone Hell

An invention by ZL1BPU (1998), S/MT-Hell is a compromise between Feld-Hell and C/MT-Hell. Like Feld-Hell, the characters are transmitted in a matrix (in fact the same sequence), but different tones are used for each row of dots in the character. The font is restricted to 7 × 5 and the white dots can be "left out," since the reception is in the frequency domain using an FFT receiver (waterfall plot). S/MT-Hell is very effective on noisy bands and may provide better sensitivity than C/MT-Hell.

Slow-Feld

Intended for beacon use rather than for QSOs, this mode is a *very* slow version of Feld-Hell. The traditional font is used, but the transmissions are at only 2 characters/minute. The biggest difference is in the receiving software—a multi-channel FFT receiver is used to coax the signal out of the noise. This approach gives very high sensitivity since the bandwidth

Windows software developed by IZ8BLY allows you to transmit and receive Feld-Hell, several MT-Hell modes and Morse using your computer soundcard.

of each channel is very narrow, and drift is compensated for with multiple receivers.

OPERATING HELLSCHREIBER

Hell signals are not common, but they make a distinctive sound that's easy to recognize. Feld-Hell, the most popular mode, generates a signal that can best be described as "scratchy CW." Using the tuning display in your software, you simply adjust your transceiver tuning until the Hell text begins painting on your monitor.

Transmitting Hellschreiber is as simple as typing the text in the appropriate window of whatever software you are using. The computer will key your radio and the text will be encoded and sent—just like RTTY or PSK31. Upper or lower sideband can be used.

You'll occasionally find Hellschreiber nets on the air (mostly on weekends). There is even a Hellschreiber contest that takes place on the first full weekend of October sponsored by the Deutscher Amateur Radio Club (DARC). When you can't seem to find a Hell signal on the air, the best thing to do is call CQ at least 10 times. If another ham with Hell capability is tuning through the band, you need to call often enough for him to find you.

Chapter NINE

MFSK

(This chapter contains excerpts from "MFSK for the New Millennium" by Murray Greenman, ZL1BPU, which appeared in the January 2001 issue of QST.*)*

MFSK is really a type of super-RTTY. The MFSK technique was developed during the heyday of teleprinter HF communications as a way to combat multipath propagation problems, providing reliable point-to-point communications with relatively simple equipment. Piccolo, for example, was used on diplomatic links between England and Singapore, and typically provided good copy for an hour after RTTY links had faded out. The technology was then electromechanical, but several very important principles were recognized at the time, and maximum advantage taken of them:

- The performance (reduced error rate) improved as the number of tones used increased.
- The performance was best when the least number of symbols is used to represent each transmitted text element.
- With a special integrating detector, tones as closely spaced as the baud rate could be uniquely detected without cross-talk.

Piccolo and Coquelet both used two symbols per text character—compare this with 7.5 for RTTY and anywhere from three to twelve for PSK31. MFSK16 uses only one symbol per signaling element! With MFSK modes the baud rate (rate at which symbols are transmitted) is rather lower than the text rate. This is because each symbol carries more information in its frequency properties than RTTY or PSK. While this is confusing, this technique has the advantage that the longer symbols are easier to detect in noise, have a lower bandwidth, and are much less

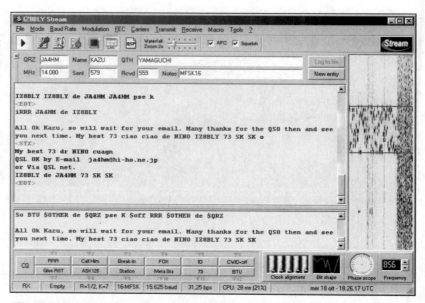

The MFSK *Stream* software for *Windows* developed by Nino Porcino, IZ8BLY.

affected by multipath timing errors.

Piccolo originally used as many as 32 tones, but the most common form used six. Coquelet generally used 12 tones. MFSK has been recently tested with as many as 64 tones, although the released version, MFSK16, uses 16 tones, and the weak signal variant MFSK8, uses 32.

The integrating detector used in Piccolo was a milestone in FSK detection techniques in its day. Without going into great detail, narrow active filters, with very high gain, were used to detect each tone. By carefully choosing the baud rate and tone channel spacing, and resetting the filters at the start of each symbol period, it was possible to reliably detect very weak tones without crosstalk to adjacent channels, and in fact the response of the adjacent channels produced a null at the point of sampling. This not only assisted with noise rejection, but prevented energy resulting from ionospheric effects on one tone from appearing in the next channel.

THE NEW APPROACH

In searching for a better way to hold reliable long path QSOs, Murray Greenman, ZL1BPU, looked at what made copy difficult with existing

An MFSK16 spectrogram. (The horizontal lines are 300 Hz apart.)

modes, and what could be done about it. It was obvious that Phase Shift Keying, unless relatively high speed, was not practical. The incidental phase errors introduced by an unstable ionosphere (particularly in polar regions) typically exceed the phase modulation of the signal. Frequency Shift Keying and On-Off Keying also perform poorly, but principally because the arrival time of signals vary, often 5-10 ms, depending on the path, and perhaps by as much as 30 ms between long and short paths. This is longer than a 22 ms RTTY symbol, and multipath reception is the reason why so many RTTY signals, even of good signal strength, will not print reliably. So, in casting around for some better method, the old MFSK techniques were revisited. In association with this research, modern PC and soundcard DSP techniques were reviewed. Putting these together, it was found that all the necessary building blocks were available to not only replicate, but enhance, the old MFSK modes, using nothing more than a PC with a soundcard.

Murray decided to kick things off by sending a specification for the new mode to many DSP, coding and software experts, and a remarkable collection of ideas and offers of assistance resulted. Nino Porcino, IZ8BLY, of Hellschreiber and MT63 fame, quickly turned the specification into reality. The result has been tested thoroughly under both real and simulated conditions. The very first QSO using this new mode was over 11,000 miles, long path on 17 meters, with 100% copy using 25 watts and dipole antennas, so the specification can't have been far wrong!

The first QSO was between IZ8BLY and ZL1BPU on June 18, 2000, and since then these two have been in communication using this mode almost every day. Most days they work 20 meters or 17 meters, using as little as 5 W.

Like IZ8BLY Hellschreiber and the well known PSK31 programs, all you need to run this software is a Pentium class PC with a soundcard, and a couple of simple cables. The first software for MFSK16 is called *Stream*, and is available for downloading on the Web. See the Resources section of this book.

THE SIGNAL

What does this new mode consist of? Well, there are 16 tones, sent one at a time at 15.625 baud, and they are spaced only 15.625 Hz apart. Each tone represents four binary bits of data. The transmission is 316 Hz wide, and has a CCIR specification of 316HF1B. It is exactly like RTTY, but with 16 closely spaced tones instead of two wider spaced tones. With a bandwidth of 316 Hz, the signal easily fits through a narrow CW filter.

The tones are continuous phase keyed, which eliminates keying noise, and the phase information can be used to determine tuning and symbol phase.

Unlike Piccolo or even PSK31, no special arrangements are made to transmit-symbol timing, since this can be recovered from the inherent properties of the signal. A most important factor is that like RTTY, the signal is constant amplitude—it does not require a linear transmitter to maintain a clean signal. Driving the transmitter too hard on MFSK16 will not make the signal any wider.

To ensure that text is received with an absolute minimum of errors, the new mode utilizes an excellent Forward Error Correction (FEC) technique, using Viterbi decoder routines by Phil Karn, KA9Q, and a clever self-synchronizing interleaver developed for MFSK by IZ8BLY. The typing rate, even with FEC, is over 40 WPM. This speed is achieved by efficient coding techniques, including a varicode similar to PSK31, providing an extended ASCII character set.

Finally, the receiver detector uses a synchronous Fast Fourier Transform (FFT) routine, a DSP technique which exactly models the original Piccolo integrating detector. The FFT is also able to provide phase information, AFC and a "waterfall" tuning display. The filter provides 4 Hz wide channels, and is easily able to separate the 16 closely spaced tones.

The signal has an amusing musical sound, is quite narrow, clean to tune across, and not unpleasant to listen to. The sound is certainly better and the bandwidth narrower than some modes on HF these days!

WORKING MFSK WITH *STREAM*

Downloading the *Stream* software (see the Resources chapter) and installing it is very simple. Fortunately the help information is also available as a separate download, so you can read that before you install.

Stream offers a generous collection of tools along the top, separate transmit and receive windows, a good collection of definable "macro" buttons, and an excellent "waterfall" tuning display. Along the bottom is a list of settings and parameters, plus the date and time. There is also a drop-down log window, for automatic logging and insertion of QSO information, and a very useful "QSP" window for relaying incoming text.

Nino's software actually includes three modes! The default mode is MFSK16 (16 tone 16 baud MFSK with FEC), and there is also slower but more sensitive MFSK8 (32 tones 8 baud with FEC). Both modes have the same bandwidth, just over 300 Hz, but sound quite different. The other new mode is one of Nino's own, 63PSKF, which is a 63 baud PSK mode, like

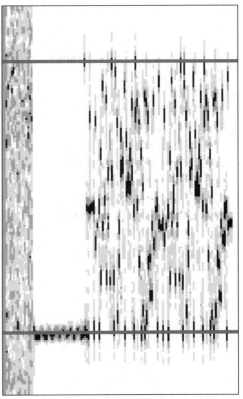

The *Stream* waterfall display in 3× zoom mode.

PSK31 but faster, and with full-time FEC. PSK63F is about 100 Hz bandwidth. The MFSK and PSK modes are complementary, as Nino's new mode is great for short path DX and local QSOs. You'll have no trouble telling them apart, and no trouble telling Nino's PSK63F from PSK31, because it is twice as wide. As a standard of comparison, the software includes PSK31 as well!

The software is very simple to use—start typing and it transmits, and press F12 to end the transmission. The trouble comes in tuning in the MFSK signals. It takes some skill and a certain patience learning to tune in MFSK, but the results are worth the effort.

Because the tones are closely spaced and the filters very narrow, you must have a very stable transceiver, and you must use the tuning provided with the software, not the transceiver tuning, and certainly not the RIT! The software allows you to tune up and down in 1 Hz steps, or click on the waterfall for exact tuning. The waterfall has a zoom function, and zoom ×3 is best.

The AFC is good, but you need to be within about 5 Hz of the right place to start with. The AFC works on the idle tone, which appears often enough for the AFC to catch it. You can see this happen as the Phase Scope comes alive. You can also manually tune by clicking on the waterfall display in just the right spot, or use the Up/Down Frequency buttons to tweak the tuning.

Tuning is done using the waterfall display. Under the lower horizontal line (red on the screen) you'll see a broad band towards the left. This is the idle carrier, the lowest of the 16 tones. This carrier is transmitted briefly at the start of each over, and returns at the end, or whenever the operator stops to think. All you need to do is center the red line on this carrier, and the AFC will keep it there. During the over, you'll see little black vertical stripes all over the waterfall, with gray "side-lobes" above and below. These are the transmitted symbols, and once again, you can adjust the software tuning so the red line centers the lowest of these symbols. Unfortunately while this is easy when the signal is already tuned, finding the correct spot on a weak signal during an over is not so simple and takes a little practice.

Once you've found the right spot, almost perfect text will start to appear on the screen, although it is delayed by some 3-4 seconds as the data trickles through the error correction system, and appears one or two words at a time.

The mode is a delight to use once you learn to tune in. The typing speed is fast, and while changeover from transmit to receive is not as fast as RTTY or Hellschreiber, it is quite good enough for ragchewing and nets.

PERFORMANCE

For QSOs using short path, say distances to 8,000 miles on 20 meters not on polar routes, MFSK16 works fine, but you may find PSK31 easier to use. If you are interested in QRP, there is not much to choose between the two. On long path, over the poles, and in really difficult conditions where QRM or instability is the major problem, MFSK16 is out on its own. It keeps going, giving almost perfect copy, without slowing down, when the signal is barely audible, has bad fades, has noticeable Doppler, multipath and even QRM. High power isn't necessary.

MFSK16 is also probably the best mode yet for digital work on the lower bands. If you are into traffic handling, or sending bulletins on 80 or 40 meters, give this mode a try. It just does not give up! 80 meters is especially prone to multipath, as RTTY and Feld-Hell users know. MFSK16 will work thousands of miles on 80 meters at night, running one watt, and with 90% perfect copy! Lightning is largely ignored.

Although not noticeably better on the low bands, MFSK8 is great to have when the band starts to die. It is definitely more sensitive than MFSK16, and although tuning is very tight, and typing speed down to 25 WPM, it will allow you to complete that QSO with almost perfect copy.

The other mode offered in the *Stream* package, PSK63F, is quite the reverse. Although not very good on long path, it is sensitive, almost as good as PSK31, and is fast (40 WPM). It uses FEC to give 100% error-free copy most of the time. It is also very easy to tune, since it is wider than PSK31 and includes excellent AFC. It is also much less affected by Doppler and drift problems. PSK63F makes a good short-haul DX mode, and would be good on VHF.

Chapter TEN

G-TOR, MT-63, Throb, Q15X25 and Domino

In this chapter we'll discuss four HF digital modes that have only small followings, yet offer interesting approaches to the problem of data communication on the HF bands.

G-TOR

Like Clover and PACTOR, G-TOR is a *proprietary* HF digital mode. In this case, the Kantronics Corporation holds the rights to G-TOR and the mode is available *only* in Kantronics multimode communications processors, primarily the KAMPlus and KAM98. It was introduced in 1994 had saw some use among hams who set up HF "mailboxes" and bulletin-board systems. Use of G-TOR has declined in recent years.

G-TOR is an acronym for *Golay-coded Teleprinting Over Radio*. Golay coding is the error-correction system created by M. J. E. Golay and used by the *Voyager* spacecraft. Sending billions of bytes of data across the Solar System required a scheme to ensure that the information could be recovered despite errors caused by interference, noise, and so on. If Golay coding could meet that challenge, the engineers at Kantronics wondered if it could be applied to digital communication on the HF bands as well.

To create G-TOR, Kantronics combined the Golay coding system with full-frame data interleaving, on-demand Huffman compression, run-length encoding, a variable data rate capability (100 to 300 bit/s) and 16-bit CRC error detection. G-TOR system timing is liberal enough to permit long-distance communication.

The G-TOR waveform consists of two phase-continuous tones (BFSK) spaced 200 Hz apart (Mark = 1600 Hz, Space = 1800 Hz). However, the system can still operate at the familiar 170-Hz shift (Mark = 2125 Hz, Space = 2295 Hz). The optimum spacing for 300-bit/s G-TOR transmissions would normally be 300 Hz. In the interest of keeping the bandwidth as close to 500 Hz as practical, some small amount of performance is traded off to save bandwidth.

One of the primary causes of reduced throughput on synchronous ARQ signals such as those used by PACTOR are errors in the acknowledgment signal (ACK). To reduce unnecessary retransmissions due to faulty ACKs, G-TOR uses *fuzzy* ACKs. This system allows receiving stations to tolerate a small number of errors in an ACK signal, rather than ignoring it completely and automatically resending the data.

With these innovations, G-TOR performs quite well despite noise, fading and interference. It is capable of passing information at two to three times the rate of PACTOR I. Under some conditions it can even rival the performance of Clover and PACTOR II.

G-TOR Frame Structure and ARQ Cycle

G-TOR operates as a synchronous ARQ mode. Regardless of transmission rate, the cycle duration is always 2.4 seconds, data frames are 1.92 seconds long, and the acknowledgments take .16 seconds. At 300 baud, each data frame contains 69 bytes of data, one control byte, and a two byte CRC. At 200 baud the frame contains 45 data bytes, and at 100 baud 21 data bytes.

Synchronization is established during the linking phase when the calling station (master) sends a G-TOR frame containing TO and FROM call signs. The information receiving station (IRS), while in standby, synchronizes to the frame by searching for its call sign. Once in step, it acknowledges such to the master and sends <link established> to its terminal. Transmission of data may then begin. Sufficient time is left between the end of the data frame and the start of the acknowledgment for propagation between stations over an HF path. A change in information flow direction (changeover) is accomplished by extending the acknowledgment bytes into a changeover frame. Once acknowledged by the other station, changeover is complete. Link quality, dictated by the number of consecutive good or bad frames received, determines link speed. The effective performance of stations, while communicating over adverse HF channels, relies on the combined use of forward error correction, interleaving and redundancy.

Prior to transmission, 300-baud frames are divided into 48 12-bit words and matched with 48 error correction words of 12 bits each. The entire 72-byte data frame is then interleaved bit-by-bit, resulting in 12 bins of 48 bits and transmitted. Upon reception by the IRS, the reverse process is carried out. The frame is synchronized, de-interleaved, decoded and checked for proper CRC. If the frame is found to be in error, the IRS will request that the matching parity frame be sent. Upon receipt, the parity frame is used in combination with the data frame in an attempt to recover the original data bits. If unsuccessful, the ARQ cycle begins again. The dispersement of noise-burst errors via interleaving and the power of the Golay code to correct 3 bits in every 24 usually results in the recovery of error-free frames.

Golay Error-Correction Coding And Interleaving

G-TOR uses extended Golay coding which is capable of correcting three or fewer errors in a received 24-bit code word. The Golay code used in G-TOR is a half-rate code, so that the encoder generates one error-correction bit (a parity bit) for every data transmitted. Interleaving is also used to correct burst errors that often occur from lightning, other noise or interference. Interleaving is the last operation performed on the frame before transmission and de-interleaving is the first operation performed upon reception. Interleaving rearranges the bits in the frame so that long error bursts can be randomized when the de-interleaving is performed. When operating at 300 symbols/sec, the interleaver reads 12-bit words into registers by columns and reads 48-bit words out of the registers by rows. The de-interleaver performs the inverse, reading the received data bits into registers by rows and extracting the original data sequence by reading the columns. A long burst of errors, for example 12-bits in duration, will be distributed into 48 separate 12-bit words before the error correction process is applied. This effectively nullifies the errors. Both data frames and parity frames are completely interleaved. In addition, by using the invertibility characteristic of Golay code words, data frames are always alternated with data frames coded in Golay parity bits. In this way, G-TOR can maintain full speed (when band conditions are good)—rather than fall to rate-1/2—receiving parity bits that can be used as data or as parity.

G-TOR in Action

G-TOR is surprisingly easy to operate. If you're familiar with PACTOR operating, G-TOR is essentially the same. When you're in the G-TOR mode, you use FEC to call CQ. This allows your transmission to be copied by as many stations as possible. If someone wants to talk to you, they respond in G-TOR using your full call sign.

When you call CQ, it sometimes helps to let stations know that you're fishing for G-TOR contacts. Here's an example of a typical G-TOR CQ:

CQ CQ CQ CQ CQ-G-TOR
CQ CQ CQ CQ CQ-G-TOR
CQ CQ CQ CQ CQ-G-TOR
DE WB8IMY WB8IMY WB8IMY
Standing by for G-TOR calls. K K

Once the G-TOR link is established, the station that called you is the ISS, or *information sending station*. It's up to him to speak first. While he is transmitting, you're the *information receiving station*, or IRS. You flip these IRS/ISS roles back and forth by sending an "over" code in a manner similar to PACTOR. And like PACTOR, G-TOR can transfer ASCII or binary information.

If you copy someone calling CQ G-TOR, you simply switch to the G-TOR standby mode. Establishing a connection is as easy as entering the word G-TOR followed by the call sign of the station you wish to contact. For example: **GTOR WB8IMY**

You can monitor the G-TOR data rate by glancing at the front panel of the KAM. When the **STA** LED is off, the rate is 100 bit/s. A flashing **STA** indicates 200 bit/s and a steady **STA** means that you're perking along at 300 bit/s. The data rates change automatically based on the quality of the link. Links always begin at 100 bit/s. If the number of correctly received frames exceeds a preset value, the receiving station will request a speed increase to 200 or 300 bit/s. If the link deteriorates, the data rate will automatically ratchet downward. You can also set the data rate manually.

The G-TOR mode supports the KAM mailbox. If you set the **ARQBBS** command *ON*, any connecting station will receive the mailbox prompt.

THROB

Throb is a sound-card mode developed by Lionel Sear, G3PPT. It takes its name from the "throbbing" sound its signals make on the air.

Throb software is only available for *Windows* and *Linux* in stand-alone applications, or in multimode programs such as *MixW* (see the Resources chapter). Throb communicates by sending either pairs of tones or single tones selected from a group of nine tones. It sends these tones within a 72 or 144-Hz bandwidth.

The current Throb application is a development of a previous version that used five tones in a 40-Hz bandwidth with the characters being coded into the permutations of three successive tones. This was slow at seven words per minute. The latest version of the program has three speeds: 1, 2 and 4 baud, allowing for a data rate of 10, 20 and 40 WPM respectively.

To operate Throb you only need a stable SSB transceiver and, of course, a computer with sound capability. The station setup is the same as with all the other sound card modes (see Chapter 2).

Throb's performance seems well suited to dealing with shifting propagation conditions, at least as well as MFSK16. Throb is rarely heard on the bands, but it has a loyal group of experimenters that continue to explore the mode. Look for Throb signals around 14080 kHz, particularly on weekends.

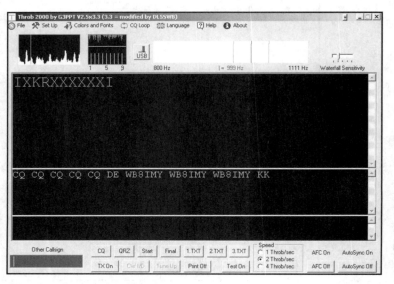

Throb software for *Windows*.

MT-63

MT-63 is a sound-card mode that has been around for several years. It was developed by Pawel Jalocha, SP9VRC.

Of all the sound-card modes, MT-63 is among the most complex in terms of structure. The transmitted data is encoded using 64 different modulated tones. There is a substantial amount of extra data in the transmission of each character, which gives the receiving station more "headroom" to recover valid information—even if 25% of the character is obliterated. This technique is called *Forward Error Correction* (FEC). Other modes use FEC (for example PACTOR FEC), but MT63 has other advantages. Unlike most HF modes where a character can be lost or changed by a single noise burst, MT63 is inherently robust because each character is spread over so many tones (to avoid interference such as other radio transmissions) and over several seconds (to avoid bursts of noise, such as lightning).

Unlike PACTOR, Clover or G-TOR, there is no "connection" process. Changeover from transmit to receive and vice-versa, however, considerably slower than most modes. It requires some skill and patience

The IZ8BLY software for MT-63.

to "break into" a QSO.

The chief disadvantage of MT-63 is its bandwidth. A typical MT-63 signal, when operating in the most robust mode, is as wide as an SSB voice signal. Also, because of the delay caused by the error correction and interleaving process, it is not possible have quick-turnaround QSOs. In other words, operation is clumsy. There is a noticeable delay of several seconds between typing a character and its final transmission

MT-63 is available in several software applications. See the Resources chapter. You can run MT-63 with any stable SSB transceiver and the typical sound-card station setup described in Chapter 2.

MT-63 Performance

Selective fading does not appear to effect MT63 reception, although the results are very visible on the waterfall. When signals are poor, MT63 transfers useful data at a normal speed. As conditions deteriorate, MT63 typically goes from almost perfect copy to almost zero copy, without much garbled text.

MT63 was effective in tests on the low bands where atmospheric noise and multi-path are the biggest problems. Especially under NVIS conditions, MT63 performs with excellent reliability, even at low power levels.

Most MT-63 software applications use waterfall displays and tuning is not difficult. Any frequency drift is usually tracked without loss of lock. Newer software is especially good in this regard.

MT-63 Operating Tips

• Send CQs using the 1-kHz interleave (see your software Help file). If your software offers CW identification, enable it.

• Use the 20-meter unofficial MT-63 calling frequency of 14.1095 kHz, upper sideband.

• Often, when working DX, the sync locks incorrectly, as evidenced by masses of garbled text, often with repeated characters (@ @ @ @ @ etc). This is the time to RESYNC. It may take several attempts for proper lock to be achieved under poor conditions.

• When starting an "over," particularly working DX, send a line of unimportant text first (e.g. call sign exchange) to allow the receiving equipment time to sync. If conditions are poor, it may take several attempts before sync is achieved.

MT-63 Technical Description

By Murray Greenman, ZL1BPU

The MT-63 modem, constructed around a high speed DSP processor, either in a dedicated external DSP unit like the Motorola EVM, or in PC software using the PC sound card, transmits 64 tones spaced 15.625 Hz apart, in the 1 kHz bandwidth. The base-band signal occupies from 500 Hz to 1500 Hz. All 64 tones are differential bipolar phase shift keyed at 10 baud. Since the Walsh FEC code is 64 bit, the character rate is the same as the symbol rate, so the throughput with FEC is ten 7-bit ASCII characters/sec (about 100 WPM). There are two other bandwidths that can be used, 500 Hz, and 2 kHz, where the tone spacing and baud rate are halved or doubled, and the throughput halves or doubles respectively. Unless otherwise indicated, this description is of the default 1 kHz version.

In addition, an optional doubling of the interleave period improves the temporal resistance (e.g. to burst noise) at the expense of increased time delay through the encoder and decoders. The different speeds are achieved by scaling all the timing factors, although the lowest carrier frequency remains constant at 500 Hz.

The user data from keyboard or file (the data code is 7-bit ASCII) is further encoded into 64 bits using a Walsh/Hadamard function to provide a highly robust FEC technique with high redundancy. The Walsh function ensures that up to 16 of the 64 bits can be corrupted, yet decoding will still produce an unambiguous result.

The MT63 signal is spread both in the time domain (temporally) and the frequency domain (spectrally). To ensure that noise bursts and other time domain interference artifacts have minimal effect, each encoded character is spread over 32 sequential symbols (3.2 sec). To ensure that frequency domain effects, such as selective fading and carrier interference have minimal effect, the character is also spread spectrally by using all the tones across the width of the transmission.

Q15X25

Q15X25 is the brainchild of Pawel Jalocha, SP9VRC, the same amateur who created MT-63. Like PACTOR, Clover and G-TOR, Q15X25 is a "connected" mode. That is to say, you converse with other stations by establishing a connection where all data is checked for errors. Any data that arrives corrupt is resent. The result is 100% copy—or no copy at all.

Q15X25 is a DSP intensive mode that operates like a packet radio

In a "long interleave" option, the spreading is over 64 symbols (6.4 sec), with consequent improvement in resistance to impulse and periodic interference, but of course double the time taken for the data to "trickle through" the Walsh encoder and decoder pipeline.

No special tuning technique is required because the signal capture logic is capable of locking with ±50 Hz frequency error (±80 Hz in the latest software). The confidence of the FEC correction system is degraded as mistuning is increased, beyond this limit, just as it would be if some of the 64 carriers were obliterated. The tracking logic will track timing and frequency error indefinitely. The decoder uses FFT techniques to define "buckets" into which carrier phase information is collected. It uses differential carrier phase detection to track phase changes introduced because of ionospheric variations.

With 10 Hz baud rate, the effect of ionospheric Doppler on signal phase within one bit time can be very serious (even more than PSK-31 because of the longer bit time), and as a result, MT63 is not a particularly good performer in this respect. The performance under these conditions is still subjectively better than PSK-31 however, because of the huge redundancy provided by the FEC system.

The receiver utilizes 64 parallel channel differential bipolar phase detectors, which ignore both frequency and amplitude variations. These provide soft solutions to the 64 Walsh decoders. Since all 64 channels generate Walsh function solutions at the same time, i.e. there are 64 parallel receiver demodulators and Walsh decoders, the receiving routine simply chooses the solution that gives the least error. This technique allows the receiver to avoid frequency ambiguity that will result if some tones are absent due to interference or fading, or if because of mis-tuning the tones are decoded as their neighbors. Newer software use further parallel receivers, allowing a greater range before mistuning degrades performance.

TNC, to provide an ARQ mode designed for AX.25 and TCP/IP on HF with speed and reliability much greater than traditional HF ARQ modems (such as 300 baud packet). It uses 15 QPSK modulated carriers separated by 125 Hz, each modulated at 83.333 baud. Q15X25 uses FEC (Forward Error Correction), and like MT-63, uses time and the frequency interleaving in order to avoid most error sources. The raw transmission data rate is typically 2500 bps.

A Q15X25 signal as seen in the *MixW* waterfall display.

Q15X25 is intended to replace HF packet by offering the same error correction benefits, but with better performance. A Q15X25 signal occupies approximately the same bandwidth as an MT-63 signal—about 2 kHz.

This is a relatively new mode and is still mostly experimental at the time of this writing. You can occasionally find Q15X25 signals at 141095 kHz, upper sideband. To try Q15X25 you'll need sound-card software, and you'll find a few listed in the Resources chapter. The popular *MixW* multimode software for *Windows* can operate Q15X25 as one of its "packet" modes by adding a support DLL and altering a few parameters. Other than the software, all you need is an SSB transceiver and the sound-card setup described in Chapter 2.

Most Q15X25 enthusiasts search for contacts by sending "beacon" transmissions. If you copy one of these beacons, you can attempt to connect by simply entering the other station's call sign into the "connect to" box in your software. The software will then attempt to establish a Q15X25 connection.

DOMINO

By Murray Greenman, ZL1BPU

Domino is an HF digital mode that debuted in early 2004. At the time of this writing, the only software that supports Domino is *ZL2AFP Domino* for *Windows*. Like other HF digital programs discussed in this book, *ZL2AFP Domino* uses your computer sound card to send and receive domino signals. It can be downloaded on the Web at **www.qsl.net/zl1bpu/MFSK/domino/dominoF.zip**.

Domino operates using an *MFSK* technique (MFSK = Multiple

The *ZL2AFP Domino* software.

Frequency Shift Keying), since MFSK offers very good immunity to interference and ionospheric effects, and is also very sensitive. However, MFSK has some disadvantages, which this unique program addresses in a special way that also makes domino easy to use, and hence ideal for beginners.

MFSK is a respected and mature technique, a generalized form of *FSK* (FSK = Frequency Shift Keying). FSK modes enjoy good immunity to noise and do not require a linear transmitter. MFSK modes were first developed in the 1950s and 1960s. The best known of these modes were Piccolo and Coquelet. Domino is in many ways similar to Coquelet, which used two tone sets, one with 8 tones, the other with four, used wide spacing, and directly coded the ITA2 character set into sequential tone pairs.

Domino employs a method of transmitting data by encoding not the actual data to be transmitted, but the *difference* between the current data and the last transmitted piece of data. Steve Olney, VK2ZTO, invented this technique for extremely narrow band transmissions. This technique is called IFK (Incremental Frequency Keying).

Domino was designed specifically for low HF bands where multipath reception is a problem, and was designed for beginners with limited skills and perhaps equipment with limited performance. Because of the double-spaced and interleaved tones, and the low data rate, domino can handle about 100 ms of multipath error (by comparison RTTY copes with less than 5 ms). Large multipath errors are common with NVIS propagation (such as 80 meters at night), and where long and short paths exist at the same time (up to 60 ms).

With a restricted character set and no FEC, a data rate of 44 WPM is achieved at a symbol rate of only 11.025 baud. This compensates for the halving of data rate due to interleaved alternated symbol pairs (16 tones are used for only three data bits instead of four). The domino mode is sufficiently robust that FEC is not really needed. Domino provides useful communications on bands impaired by multipath where RTTY would not give readable copy.

SIGNAL RECOGNITION

It is very important for digital modes to be easily recognized and identified. Thus, the onus is on the designer to provide something unique for each new mode. Domino can be identified by the insistent "falling" that is heard when the program is idle or between words. It sounds a bit like a flock of seagulls calling (or is it domino tiles falling?). The three different speeds can be identified by ear or on the waterfall, by bandwidth or clarity of dots.

On the waterfall display, the signal looks like a series of downward pointing stair-steps, in a very regular pattern. In addition, the waterfall display will be blurry if the received mode is incorrect, but will be very sharp when it is correct. If the signal is inverted, it will have a "rising" stair-step characteristic.

ZL2AFP DOMINO SOFTWARE

The program should work on any PC with *Windows 95* or later, provided it has a Sound Blaster compatible sound card. A computer clock speed of 120 MHz and 32 MB of memory should suffice. You will also require suitable cables or an interface for connection between the sound card and the HF transceiver (see Chapter 2).

Receiving

The domino program automatically starts in receive mode. The **Receive** Control Button will be grayed-out. The waterfall and tuning displays will be active. With the AGC off, adjust the audio level (receiver gain at a comfortable level), then use the **Input** Menu to set the **Line In** Level so the green line just moves on background noise, and there is some sign of the noise on the waterfall display. Set the AGC back on. Tune in a signal, and adjust the receiver tuning until the entire signal is within the area between the yellow lines on the waterfall.

If more convenient, adjust the waterfall up and down. This can be achieved by left clicking on the waterfall and dragging the display up or down.

If clear text in the Receive Window does not result, check that the entire signal is between the yellow lines, check that the signal is the "right way up" (correct sideband) with a falling sound, try receiving with AGC off and manual level adjustment, and finally check that it is the correct mode!

If the level is too high, the waterfall will smear and individual dots will be indistinct. Poor print quality can also result if there is excessive multi-path on the signal. This will be observed on the waterfall as patches of wider than normal tones (vertical stripes or curved lines rather than dots). These effects often occur at a point of fade, and can happen occasionally to frequently. If this happens frequently during a QSO, change to a lower speed as soon as possible, and also be alert for the other operator changing speed (you will hear the tones change).

As the signal drifts, you can adjust the receiver tuning slowly without losing copy, or just drag the waterfall in the required direction to center the signal. If your receiver step-tunes in 10Hz or smaller steps, you should not lose copy, but if the tuning is in 100Hz steps or greater, it will be better to drag the waterfall for tuning. The waterfall tuning has 1Hz resolution. In order to transmit back on about the same frequency, make sure the bottom of the received signal is approximately at 1100Hz (preferably adjust receiver tuning rather than dragging the waterfall).

Transmitting

While still receiving, you can type in the Transmit Window, cut and paste text, or press macro buttons, so text will go into the TX Window. This text will be transmitted immediately when the transmitter starts, followed by anything you subsequently type in the TX buffer. You can edit text in the buffer before it is sent, even copy, cut and paste, no matter whether the text was typed, copied from the RX window, or from the macros. You can also do this while transmitting, but you'll need to be fairly quick! Backspace is handy, as it works "over the air"—you can correct text already sent by deleting at the other end!

To start transmitting domino, simply press the **Transmit** Control Button. This will now be grayed-out, and the transmitter signal will appear from the sound card. While the software idles (no text sent), adjust the audio level sensitivity for correct operation. If using the microphone input for transmit audio, it is best to leave the MIC level setting in the normal SSB position and adjust the transmit power level using the sound card applet. Use the **Output** Menu to set the **Wave** Level and the **Volume Control** to give the correct transmitter drive.

When all the text to be sent has gone (it will appear in red in the Rx Window), the transmitter will idle, sending blank characters used to keep the receiver in sync and creating the characteristic domino falling sound. As soon as new text is typed, this will be sent in place of the idling. At the end of an over, wait for the last text to be sent, recognize a few idles at the end, and then press the **Receive** Control Button. The transmitter will stop immediately, and the receiver will start. Any characters remaining in the TX buffer (the Transmit Window) will remain there unsent until the start of the next over.

Chapter ELEVEN

HF Digital Contesting

Nothing tests your equipment and operating skills like a contest. If you have shortcomings in your antenna system, you're going to discover them very quickly. If your transceiver can't seem to handle the crunch of dozens of signals in proximity, it will become painfully apparent within minutes. If you need better logging or contest software, the first hour of a contest will provide a powerful motivation to upgrade!

Some hams shun contesting because they assume they don't have the time or hardware necessary to win—and they are probably right. But winning is *not* the objective for most contesters. You enter a contest to do the best you can, to push yourself and your station to whatever limits you wish. The satisfaction at the end of a contest comes from the knowledge that you were part of the glorious frenzy, and that you gave it your best shot!

Contesting also has a practical benefit. If you're an award chaser, you can work many desirable stations during an active contest. During the ARRL RTTY Roundup, for example, some hams have worked enough international stations to earn a RTTY DXCC. Jump into the North American RTTY QSO Party and you stand a good chance of earning your Worked All States in a single weekend.

Always remember that contesting is ultimately about *enjoyment*. The thrill of the contest chase gets your heart pumping. The little triumphs, like working that distant station even though he was deep in the noise, will bring smiles to your face.

You'll make a number of friends along the way, too. Why do you think it is called the "brotherhood of contesting"?

DIGITAL CONTESTING TIPS FOR THE "LITTLE PISTOL"

If you are like most amateurs, your station falls into the Little Pistol category. Mine does, too. The Little Pistol station usually includes a low- to medium-priced 100-W transceiver feeding an omnidirectional antenna such as a dipole, vertical, end-fed wire and so on. Even if you are blessed with a beam antenna on a tower or rooftop, in all likelihood you are still a Little Pistol.

At the opposite end of the spectrum are the Big Gun stations.

Digital Contest Calendar

See *QST* or the *National Contest Journal* for complete rules.

Month	Date	Contest
January	1st	SARTG New Years RTTY Contest
January	First full weekend	ARRL RTTY Roundup
January	Last full weekend	BARTG RTTY Sprint
February	First full weekend	FMRE RTTY Contest
February	Second weekend	WorldWide RTTY WPX Contest
March	Second weekend	North American RTTY Sprint
March	Third weekend	BARTG WW RTTY Contest
April	First full weekend	EA WW RTTY Contest
April	Third weekend	TARA PSK31 Rumble
April	Fourth full weekend	SP DX RTTY Contest
May	First full weekend	ARI International DX Contest
May	Second weekend	VOLTA WW RTTY Contest
June	Second weekend	ANARTS WW RTTY Contest

They have multiple beams on tall towers, phased array antennas on the lower bands, incredibly long Beverage receiving antennas and more. They own high-end (read: expensive) transceivers that boast razor-sharp selectivity, and they usually couple them to 1.5 kW linear amplifiers.

So how does a Little Pistol go about beating a Big Gun in a digital contest? With rare exceptions, he can't. Banging heads with a Big Gun station is usually an exercise in futility. He is going to hear more stations, and more stations are going to hear him. Focus, instead, on using your wits and equipment to get the best score possible. You probably won't beat a Big Gun, but you could make him sweat!

Month	Date	Contest
July	Third weekend	**North American RTTY QSO Party**
July	Fourth full weekend	**Russian WW RTTY Contest**
August	Third weekend	**SARTG WW RTTY Contest**
August	Last full weekend	**SCC RTTY Championship**
September	First full weekend	**CCCC PSK31 Contest**
September	Last full weekend	**CQ WW RTTY Contest**
October	First full weekend	**TARA PSK31 Rumble**
October	First full weekend	**DARC International Hellschreiber Contest**
October	Third weekend	**JARTS WW RTTY Contest**
November	Second weekend	**WAE RTTY Contest**
December	First full weekend	**TARA RTTY Sprints**
December	Second weekend	**OK RTTY DX Contest**

Check Your Antenna

How long has it been since you've inspected your antenna? Is everything clean and tight? And have you considered trying a different antenna? Contests are terrific testing environments for antenna designs. For example, if you've been using a dipole for a while, why not try a loop? Just set up the antenna temporarily for the duration of the contest and see what happens.

Check Your Equipment

If you are having problems with RF getting into your processor or soundcard, fix these glitches *before* you find yourself in a contest! Also, consider spending $100 or so to install a 500-Hz IF filter in your radio if it doesn't have one already. Outboard audio DSP filters are helpful to cut down the signal clutter, but a good IF filter will make a world of difference in a contest environment. Finally, check your computer and software. Make sure you understand the program completely. Set up any "canned" messages/responses and test them before the contest begins.

Understand Propagation

If you are participating in a DX contest, is it a good idea to prowl the 40-meter band in the middle of the day? No, it isn't. Forty meters is only good for DX contacts after sundown. If you are hunting Europeans or Africans on 10 or 15 meters, when is the best time to look for them? The answer is late morning to early afternoon.

In other words, let propagation conditions guide your contest strategy. Your goal is to squeeze the most out of every band at the right time of day. For example, I might start the ARRL RTTY Roundup on 10 meters and then bounce between 10, 15 and 20 meters until sunset. After sundown, I'll concentrate on 20 and 40 meters. In the late night and the wee hours of the morning, I'll probably limit myself to 40 and 80 meters.

In some contests you can enter as a single-band station. Which band should you choose? That depends on the contest and your equipment. If you have a 15-meter beam and you are entering a DX RTTY contest, it makes sense to concentrate on 15 meters, even though you'll probably find yourself with nothing to do in the late evening after the band shuts down. Twenty meters makes sense as the ultimate "around the clock" band, but it is often very crowded during contests and populated with Big Gun stations. In some instances you may find it more "profitable" to concentrate your efforts on another band without so many signals.

Hunting and Pouncing vs. "Running"

The common sense rule of thumb is that a Little Pistol station should only hunt and pounce. That means that you patrol the bands, watching for "CQ CONTEST" on your monitor, and pouncing on any signals you find. The Big Guns, on the other hand, often set up shop on clear frequencies and start blasting CQs. If conditions are favorable, they'll be hauling in contacts like a commercial fishing trawler! This is known as *running*.

In many cases Little Pistols are probably wasting valuable time by attempting to run. There are situations, however, where running *does* make sense. If you've pounced on every signal you can find on a particular band, try sending a number of CQs yourself to catch some of the other pouncers. If you send five CQs in a row and no one responds, don't bother to continue. Move to another band and resume pouncing.

Seek Ye the Multipliers

Every contest has multipliers. These are US states, DXCC countries, ARRL sections, grid squares and so on, depending on the rules of the contest. A multiplier is valuable because it multiplies your total score.

Let's say that DXCC countries are multipliers for our hypothetical contest. You've amassed a total of 200 points so far, and in doing so you made contacts with 50 different DXCC countries.

$200 \times 50 = 10,000$ points

Those 50 multipliers made a huge difference in your score! Imagine what the score would have been if you had only worked 10 multipliers?

If given a choice between chasing a station that won't give me a new multiplier and pursuing one that *will*, I'll spend much more time trying to bag the new multiplier.

Choose the Right Mode

Many contests allow the use of all HF digital modes, but RTTY is by far the most popular. Yes, you can probably make some contacts during the ARRL RTTY Roundup using PACTOR, for example, but you'll miss RTTY contact points while doing so. As the saying goes, "When in Rome do as the Romans do."

There are some contests that are devoted to one mode in particular. With the increasing popularity of PSK31, for example, PSK31-*only* contests are springing up.

CONTEST SOFTWARE

No one says you have to use software to keep track of your contest contacts, but it certainly makes life easier! One of the fundamental elements of any contest program is the ability to check for duplicate contacts or *dupes*. Working the same station that you just worked an hour ago is not only embarrassing, it is a waste of time. The better contest programs feature automatic dupe checking. When you enter the call sign in the logging window, the software instantly checks your log and warns you if the contact qualifies as a dupe. The more sophisticated programs "know" the rules of all the popular digital contests and they can quickly determine whether a contact is truly a dupe under the rules of the contest in question. Some contests, for example, allow you to work stations only *once*, regardless of the band. Other contests will allow you to work stations once per band.

A good software package will also help you track multipliers. It will display a list of multipliers you've worked, or show the ones you still need to find.

Any of the contest software packages advertised in *QST* and the *National Contest Journal* will function well. To minimize headaches, however, my suggestion is to stick with software written specifically for digital contesting. There are two popular digital contesting software packages on the market today:

Ham System is a *DOS* digital contest package popular with European amateurs.

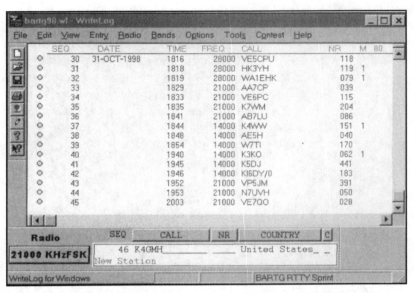

WriteLog is **Windows** software that not only logs, it includes the ability to send and receive RTTY and PSK31 using your computer soundcard.

• OH2GI *Ham System* is another *DOS* package similar to *RTTY* in many respects. *Ham System* is particularly popular among European contesters and is compatible with almost every known modem and processor. See the *Ham System* Web site at **www.kolumbus.fi/jukka.kallio/**.

• *WriteLog* by Ron Stailey, K5DJ, is a full-featured *Windows*-based software package with an interesting twist. While *WriteLog* can be used with any processor or modem, it also has the *built-in* ability to send and receive RTTY and PSK31 using your soundcard. Like *RTTY*, *WriteLog* offers automatic dupe checking and flagging, multiplier displays, radio control, canned messages and more. See the *WriteLog* site on the Web at **www.writelog.com/**.

Chapter TWELVE

Resources

MULTIMODE COMMUNICATION PROCESSORS

- HAL Communications, 1201 W. Kenyon Rd, Urbana, IL 61801-0365; tel 217-367-7373; **www.halcomm.com/**
- Kantronics, 1202 East 23rd St, Lawrence, KS 66046; tel 785-842-7745; **www.kantronics.com/**
- MFJ Enterprises, PO Box 494, Mississippi State, MS 39762; tel 601-323-5869; **www.mfjenterprises.com/**
- Timewave Technology Inc, 58 Plato Blvd E., St Paul, MN 55107; 651-222-4858; **www.timewave.com/**
- SCS, Roentgenstr 36, D-63454 Hanau, Germany; **www.scs-ptc.com/**

SOUND CARD SOFTWARE

A few words about Web addresses: Every attempt was made to ensure that the following Web addresses were active at the time this edition was published. Web addresses change with astonishing frequency, however, so don't be surprised if a particular address is suddenly "broken." The person who manages the site may have removed it from the Web, or the site may have been moved to another address. When you encounter a faulty address, try using a Web search engine such as Google (**www.google.com**) to locate the site.

Windows

RTTY
DSP-CW: **www.zicom.se/dsp/index.html**
HamScope: **www.qsl.net/hamscope/**
MixW: **www.mixw.net**
MMTTY: **www.qsl.net/mmhamsoft/**
MultiPSK: **members.aol.com/f6cte/index.htm**
RCKRTTY: **www.rckrtty.de/**
SkySweeper: **www.skysweep.com/skysweep.html**
TruTTY: **www.dxsoft.com/**
WinWarbler: **www.qsl.net/winwarbler/**

PSK31
DigiPan: **www.digipan.net/**
HamScope: **www.qsl.net/hamscope/**
MixW: **www.mixw.net**
MultiPSK: **members.aol.com/f6cte/index.htm**
PSK31 Deluxe: **hb9drv.ham-radio.ch/**
RCKRTTY: **www.rckrtty.de/**
SkySweeper: **www.skysweep.com/skysweep.html**
W1SQLPSK: **www.faria.net/w1sql/**
WinPSKse: **www.winpskse.com/**
WinWarbler: **www.qsl.net/winwarbler/**

Hell
HamScope: **www.qsl.net/hamscope/**
IZ8BLY Hellschreiber: **www.geocities.com/iz8bly/
index.htm**
MixW: **www.mixw.net**
MultiPSK: **members.aol.com/f6cte/index.htm**
SkySweeper: **www.skysweep.com/skysweep.html**

MFSK16
HamScope: **www.qsl.net/hamscope/**
MixW: **www.mixw.net**
SkySweeper: **www.skysweep.com/skysweep.html**
Stream: **www.geocities.com/iz8bly/**

Throb
MixW: **www.mixw.net**
Throb26: **www.lsear.freeserve.co.uk/page3.html**
Throbx2: **www.lsear.freeserve.co.uk/page3.html**

MT-63	*MixW*: **www.mixw.net**
	MT63 Terminal: **www.geocities.com/iz8bly/**
Q15X25	*MixW*: **www.mixw.net**

MacOS

| RTTY, PSK31, Hell | *Multimode*: **www.blackcatsystems.com/** |
| | **software/multimode.html** |

Linux

RTTY	*LinPSK*: **linpsk.sourceforge.net/**
PSK31	*KPSK*: **linkt.de/1409/projects/kpsk/**
	LinPSK: **linpsk.sourceforge.net/**
MFSK16	*gmfsk*: **www.freshports.org/comms/gmfsk/**
MT-63	*LinuxMT63*:**www.qsl.net/zl1bpu/MT63/Software.**
	html#LINUX
Q15X25	*Newqpsk*: **he.fi/pub/ham/unix/linux/ax25/newqpsk/**
Hell	*gmfsk*: **www.freshports.org/comms/gmfsk/**
Throb	*gmfsk*: **www.freshports.org/comms/gmfsk/**

THE FCC OPENS THE DOOR IN 1995

Prior to 1995, the only legal HF digital modes were those that used standard ASCII codes. That severely limited the development of new modes that depended on more efficient coding. In 1995 the FCC declared that any new codes were legal as long as they were published in the public domain (and as long as the new modes that resulted did not otherwise violate Part 97 rules).

What follows is the actual FCC report. Although it discusses CLOVER, G-TOR and PACTOR specifically, this announcement opened the door to greater digital innovations.

FEDERAL COMMUNICATIONS COMMISSION
47 CFR Part 97
[DA 95-2106]
Use of CLOVER, G-TOR, and PacTOR Digital Codes
AGENCY: Federal Communications Commission.
ACTION: Final rule; interpretation.

SUMMARY: On October 2, 1995, the Chief, Wireless Tele-communications Bureau adopted an Order that clarified that amateur stations may use any digital code that has its technical characteristics publicly documented. The amendments were necessary because some amateur operators have expressed concern about the propriety of using the CLOVER, G-TOR, and PacTOR codes on the High Frequency amateur service bands.
EFFECTIVE DATE: November 1, 1995.
FOR FURTHER INFORMATION CONTACT:
William T. Cross of the Wireless Telecommunications Bureau at (202) 418-0680.
SUPPLEMENTARY INFORMATION:
Order
Adopted: October 2, 1995
Released: October 11, 1995
  By the Chief, Wireless Telecommunications Bureau:
  1. This Order amends Section 97.309(a) of the Commission's Rules, 47 CFR 97.309(a), to clarify that amateur stations may use any digital code that has its technical characteristics publicly documented. This action was initiated by a letter from the American Radio Relay League, Inc. (ARRL).
  2. The ARRL states that some amateur operators have expressed concern about the propriety of using the CLOVER, G-TOR, and PacTOR codes on the High Frequency (HF) amateur service bands. [CLOVER, G-TOR, and PacTOR are different techniques currently used by many amateur operators to increase the efficiency of digital communications transmitted on the HF portion of the radio spectrum.] This is due to the fact that Section 97.309(a) appears to authorize only the Baudot, AMTOR, and ASCII codes on the HF bands. [On the Very High Frequency and shorter wavelength bands, the rules authorize the use of any unspecified digital code provided the emission does not exceed a specified bandwidth. See Sections 97.307(f) (5)-(7) of the Commission's Rules, 47 CFR Secs.

97.307(f)(5)-(7).] The ARRL states that it has worked with the developers of CLOVER, G-TOR, and PacTOR to document the technical characteristics of these codes. It requests, therefore, that we amend Section 97.309(a) of the Commission's Rules to specifically authorize CLOVER, G-TOR, and PacTOR to remove any doubt about the permissibility of their use.

3. The primary purpose of CLOVER, G-TOR, and PacTOR is to facilitate communications using already-authorized digital codes, emission types, and frequency bands. The technical characteristics of CLOVER, G-TOR, and PacTOR have been documented publicly for use by amateur operators, and commercial products are readily available that facilitate the transmission and reception of communications incorporating these codes. [See Technical Descriptions CLOVER, G-TOR, PACTOR, published by the American Radio Relay League, Inc. (1995).] Including CLOVER, G-TOR, and PacTOR in the rules will not conflict with our objective of preventing the use of codes or ciphers intended to obscure the meaning of the communication. [The HF bands are widely used for international communications. Number 2732 Sec. 2.(1) of Article 32 Section I of the International Telecommunications Union Radio Regulations requires that transmissions between amateur stations of different countries by made in plain language. Section 97.113(a)(4) of the Commission's Rules, 47 CFR Sec. 97.113(a)(4), therefore, prohibits amateur stations from transmitting messages in codes or ciphers intended to obscure the meaning thereof.] We agree, therefore, that it would be helpful to the amateur service community for the rules to specifically authorize amateur stations to transmit messages and data using these and similar digital codes. Accordingly, we are amending Section 97.309(a) to clarify the rules as requested by the ARRL.

4. Because the rule amendment adopted herein is interpretative in nature, and clarifies the existing amateur service rules, the notice and comment provisions of Section 553(b) of the Administrative Procedure Act, 5 U.S.C. Sec. 553(b), do not apply, and it is not subject to the publication or service requirements of Section 553(d) of the Administrative Procedure Act, 5 U.S.C. Sec. 553(d).

5. We certify that the Regulatory Flexibility Act of 1980 does not apply to the amended rule because there will not be any significant economic impact on a substantial number of small business entities, as defined by Section 601(3) of the Regulatory Flexibility Act. The amateur service may not be used to transmit communications for compensation, for the pecuniary benefit of the station control operator or the station

control operator's employer, or for communications, on a regular basis, which could reasonably be furnished through other radio services. See 47 CFR Sec. 97.113. The Secretary shall send a copy of this Order, including the certification, to the Chief Counsel for Advocacy of the Small Business Administration in accordance with paragraph 605(b) of the Regulatory Flexibility Act, Pub. L. No. 96-354, 94 Stat. 1164, 5 U.S.C. Secs. 601-612 (1981).

6. Accordingly, IT IS ORDERED that effective upon publication in the Federal Register, Part 97 of the Commission's Rules, 47 CFR Part 97, IS AMENDED as set forth below. This action is taken under the authority delegated to the Chief, Wireless Telecommunications Bureau, in section 0.331(a)(1) of the Commission's Rules, 47 CFR Sec. 0.331(a)(1).

Federal Communications Commission
Regina M. Keeney,
Chief, Wireless Telecommunications Bureau.
Rule Changes
Part 97 of Chapter I of Title 47 of the Code of Federal Regulations is amended as follows:
PART 97–AMATEUR RADIO SERVICE
1. The authority citation for Part 97 continues to read as follows:
Authority: 48 Stat. 1066, 1082, as amended; 47 U.S.C. 154, 303. Interpret or apply 48 Stat. 1064-1068, 1081-1105, as amended; 47 U.S.C. 151-155, 301-609, unless otherwise noted.
2. Section 97.309 is amended by adding paragraph (a)(4) to read as follows:
Sec. 97.309 RTTY and data emission codes.
(a) * * *
(4) An amateur station transmitting a RTTY or data emission using a digital code specified in this paragraph may use any technique whose technical characteristics have been documented publicly, such as CLOVER, G-TOR, or PacTOR, for the purpose of facilitating communications.

Appendix

Technical Descriptions

In 1989, the League issued a challenge to amateurs to develop ways of improving the performance of packet radio in the high frequency bands. Instead of responding with improvements to AX.25 packet radio, designers came up with different strategies to provide for efficient HF data communication technologies, namely PACTOR, PACTOR II, CLOVER, G-TOR, PSK31 and, most recently, CLOVER-2000. These initiatives by individuals and design teams in the United States, Germany and the UK quickly gained acceptance. Products and software supporting these technologies are currently available and in use by radio amateurs worldwide. These systems have found applications by other radio services seeking improvements in HF communications efficiency.

The technical descriptions that follow are intended to document the manifest technical characteristics of these systems. They are not intended as complete system definitions. The ARRL also maintains an archive of technical descriptions on its Web site at **www.arrl.org/FandES/field/ regulations/techchar/**. See this site for the latest updates.

These systems carry no specific endorsement by the League except to applaud the innovative work by their developers. We encourage further study and development of HF digital communications in the amateur services.

CLOVER

1. INTRODUCTION

CLOVER is a digital communications mode that conveys 8-bit digital data over narrow-band high-frequency radio. It can also transfer ASCII text and executable computer files without using the additional control characters required in other digital modes, which decrease throughput. It measures signal conditions, and automatically changes modulation format and data throughput to match current link quality. Reed-Solomon data encoding provides forward error correction (FEC) within each data block to repair many errors without the need for retransmission.

2. WAVEFORM

The CLOVER waveform consists of four tone pulses, each of which is 125 Hz wide, spaced at 125 Hz centers. The four tone pulses are sequential, with only one tone being present at any instant and each tone lasting 8 ms. Each frame consists of four tone pulses lasting a total of 32 ms, so the base modulation rate of a CLOVER signal is always 31.25 symbols per second. Data is conveyed by changing the phase and/or amplitude of successive pulses at the same frequency. These changes are made only at the instants midway between the peaks of two successive pulses when their amplitudes are zero. The measured CLOVER modulation spectra is tightly confined within a 500 Hz bandwidth, with outside edges suppressed 50 dB to prevent interference to adjacent frequencies. Unlike other modulation schemes, the CLOVER modulation spectra is the same for all modulation formats. Additional key parameters of CLOVER modulation include a symbol rate of 31.25 symbol/s (regardless of the type of modulation being used), 2:1 voltage (6 dB power) crest factor, and a ITU-R emission designator of 500H J2 DEN or 500H J2 BEN.

3. TRANSMISSION PROTOCOLS

CLOVER normally operates over half-duplex links and uses a Reed-Solornon algorithm to provide FEC. This FEC may be used alone in FEC mode or combined with an Automatic Repeat reQuest (ARQ) protocol in ARQ mode to acknowledge each individual data block. The ARQ mode provides an effective adaptive control system which constantly measures the signal-to-noise ratio, frequency offset, phase dispersion, and errors on each block of received data. CLOVER evaluates these measured parameters and selects the best modulation format for the respective propagation conditions. The receive modem sends commands to the transmitting modem indicating which modulation format should be used for the next transmission. This process ensures selection of an optimum modulation format, allowing CLOVER to operate even with multipath and other HF propagation impairments.

4. REED-SOLOMON ERROR DETECTION AND CORRECTION ALGORITHM

Reed-Solomon FEC is used in all CLOVER modes. This is a powerful byte and block oriented error-correction technique, not available in other common HF data modes, and it can allow the receiving station to correct errors without requiring a repeat transmission. Errors are detected on octets of data rather than on the individual bits themselves. This error correction technique is ideally suited for HF use in which errors due to fades or interferences are often "bursty" (short-lived) but cause total destruction of a number of sequential data bits. Error correction at the receiver is determined by "check" bytes which are inserted in each block by the transmitter. The receiver uses these check bytes to reconstruct data which has been damaged during transmission. The capacity of the error corrector to fix errors is limited and set by how many check bytes are sent per block.

Check bytes are also "overhead" on the signal and their addition effectively reduces the efficiency and therefore the "throughput rate" at which user data is passed between transmitter and receiver. Efficiencies of 60%, 75%, or 90% can be invoked by using successively lower levels of Reed-Solomon encoding for error correction, or 100% efficiency by bypassing this algorithm. Better propagation conditions do not require as much error correction, which means the amount of overhead decreases and the efficiency increases.

5. SIGNAL CHARACTERISTICS

CLOVER normally uses six different modulation formats which are automatically selected to best compensate for the propagation conditions.

These formats are described in the following chart:

CLOVER MODULATION FORMATS

Modulation	Description	Data Rate (bps)
2DPSM	Dual-diversity Binary Phase Shift Modulation (PSM)	62.5
BPSM	Binary PSM	125
QPSM	Quadrinary PSM	250
8PSM	8-level PSM	375
SPSM/2ASM	8-level PSM, 2-level Amplitude Shift Modulation	500
16PSM/4ASM	16-level PSM, 4-level Amplitude Shift Modulation	750

6. IDENTIFICATION

Call signs are exchanged during linking, and each station identifies every few minutes, all automatically.

7. CLOVER CONTROL BLOCK (CCB)

Each transmission uses a CLOVER Control Block (CCB) to provide synchronization and mode information. Only one CCB is sent per transmitter-ON cycle. The CCB is always sent using a 17-octet block size and a 60% Reed-Solomon encoder efficiency. The CCB uses 2DPSM modulation in the FEC mode and BPSM modulation in the ARQ mode. The CCB is followed by one or more Error Corrector Blocks (ECBs) of data. In FEC mode, the CCB serves as a preamble to the data block which announces the modulation format and the sending station call sign. In ARQ mode, the CCB follows transmission of one or more data blocks and is used to announce the modulation format to be used by the other station during its next transmission.

8. ERROR CORRECTION BLOCK (ECB)

The data field contains one or more ECBs of error-correction encoded data. One of the variable parameters in CLOVER modulation is the length of the ECB which can be 17, 51, 85, or 255 octets long, always sent at a fixed channel rate of 31.25 bit/s. This is analogous to packet length. However, in this case, block length and the number of Reed-Solomon correctable errors are proportional, with longer blocks being able to correct more errors without requiring repeat transmissions. The effective data rate varies with the type of modulation and the encoder efficiency, going up to 750 bit/s under optimum conditions.

9. FEC MODE

This mode allows a sending station to transmit data to one or more receiving stations. FEC mode is a one-way transmission that cannot repeat transmissions for error correction or use adaptive waveform selection. Therefore, the sending station must choose a transmitting modulation format in advance and assume that conditions between the sending station and all other stations are adequate for the chosen mode. The Reed-Solomon algorithm is used to provide receive error correction in FEC mode with a 60% code rate. Both BPSM and QPSM modulations use 85-character blocks, and the default modulation format is 2DPSM in FEC mode.

The first CCB frame begins with 2.048 seconds of carrier. A 32-ms carrier-off gap immediately follows this frame and each of the following frames. This first CCB frame becomes identical to all of the following (recurrent) CCB frames from this point on. The next frame sent is a 64-bit synchronization sequence which also lasts 2.048 seconds. All subsequent blocks are immediately preceded by a 32-ms reference tone pulse sequence. The CCB is next, and it is followed by from 3 to 9 ECBs.

10. ARQ MODE

ARQ is a two-way point-to-point mode which provides fully adaptive and error-corrected communications between two stations that are linked together. As in the case of FEC, a varying number of ECBs are sent in each ARQ time frame. The number of ECBs and other timing parameters are adjusted so that the total time for each ARQ frame is exactly 19.488 seconds, regardless of modulation waveform combination used. The full advantages of adaptive waveform control and error correction via repeat transmission are provided to these two stations. Data is communicated between both ARQ stations by adding a series of ECBs of data following the CCB. Although the CCB's waveform parameters remain fixed, the waveform of the ECBs is adaptively adjusted to match current propagation conditions. The throughput rate during ECB transinissions is generally much higher than that used for the CCB, because the ECB uses longer blocks and high-rate modulation waveforms to expedite data transfer. All ARQ link maintenance operations are performed at the CCB level.

ARQ ECBs are always 255 bytes long. The Reed-Solomon code rate is set for 150, 188, or 226 8-bit data bytes per ECB depending upon the ARQ bias selected (Robust, Normal, or Fast, respectively). The default bias setting is Robust. Both stations send CCB frames, which last 2.720 seconds. A limited amount of data may be exchanged within the CCBs (called Chat Mode), although large quantities of data are transferred through the ECBs. Unlike packet radio, CLOVER selectively repeats only those blocks which fail Reed-Solomon correction, not all blocks following a failed block. ARQ is an adaptive mode that does not use 2DPSM modulation.

11. MONITORING CAPABILITY

LISTEN mode permits additional stations to monitor all traffic between linked ARQ mode stations. Call signs of all CLOVER stations being monitored are also displayed, since CLOVER stations automatically identify every few minutes.

CLOVER REFERENCES

Ford, Steve: "HAL Communications PCI-4000 CLOVER-II Data Controller" (Product Review), *QST*, American Radio Relay League, Newington, CT, May 1993, pp. 71-73.

HAL Communications: "CLOVER Glossary," Engineering Document E2000, Rev. D, HAL Communications Corp., Urbana, IL, November 1992.

HAL Communications: "PCI-4000/CLOVER-II Interface Specifications," Engineering Document E2001, Rev. G, HAL Communications Corp., Urbana, IL, March 1993.

HAL Communications: "PCI-4000 CLOVER-II Data Modem Reference Manual" and "PC-CLOVER Operator's Manual," HAL Communications Corp., Urbana, IL, November 1992.

Henry, George W. and Ray C. Petit: "CLOVER - Fast Data on HF Radio," *CQ*, CQ Communications, Hicksville, NY, May 1992, pp. 40-44.

Henry, George W. and Ray C. Petit: "HF Radio Data Communication: CW to CLOVER," *Communications Quarterly*, CQ Communications, Hicksville, NY, Spring 1992, pp. 11 -24.

Horzepa, Stan (ed); George W. Henry and Ray C. Petit: "CLOVER Development Continues," "Gateway," *QEX*, American Radio Relay League, Newington, CT, March 1992, pp. 12-14.

Petit, Ray C.: "CLOVER is Here," *RTTY Journal*, Fountain Valley, CA; January 1991, pp. 16-18; February 1991, pp. 12-13; March 1991, pp. 16-17; April 1991, p.10.

Petit, Ray C.: "CLOVER Status Report," *RTTY Journal*, Fountain Valley, CA, January 1992, pp. 8-9.

Petit, Ray C.: "The 'CLOVERLEAF' Performance-Oriented HF Data Communication System," *QEX*, American Radio Relay League, Newington, CT, July 1990, pp. 9-12.

Townsend, Jay: "CLOVER - PCI-4000," *RTTY Journal*, Fallbrook, CA, April 1993, pp. 3-4; May/June 1993, p. 20.

CLOVER-2000

1. INTRODUCTION & WAVEFORM

CLOVER-2000 is a faster version of CLOVER (about four times faster) that uses eight tone pulses, each of which is 250 Hz wide, spaced at 250-Hz centers, contained within a 2 kHz bandwidth between 500 and 2,500 Hz. The eight tone pulses are sequential, with only one tone being present at any instant and each tone lasting 2 ms. Each frame consists of eight tone pulses lasting a total of 16 ms, so the base modulation rate of a CLOVER-2000 signal is always 62.5 symbols per second (regardless of the type of modulation being used). Its CCIR emission designation is 2K0H J2 DEN or 2K0H J2 BEN and it has a 2:1 voltage (6 dB power) crest factor. CLOVER-2000's maximum raw data rate is 3,000 bits per second. Allowing for overhead, CLOVER-2000 can deliver error-corrected data over a standard HF SSB radio channel at up to 1,994 bits per second, or 249 characters (8-bit bytes) per second. These are the uncompressed data rates; the maximum throughput is typically doubled for plain text if compression is used.

2. CLOVER SIMILARITIES

CLOVER-2000 is similar to the previous version of CLOVER. The transmission protocols and Reed-Solomon error detection and correction algorithm sections in the original CLOVER technical description are therefore not repeated here. The original descriptions of the CLOVER Control Block (CCB) and Error Correction Block (ECB) still apply for CLOVER-2000, except for the higher data rates inherent to CLOVER-2000. Just like CLOVER, all data sent via CLOVER-2000 is encoded as 8-bit data bytes and the error-correction coding and modulation formatting processes are transparent to the data stream — every bit of source data is delivered to the receiving terminal without modification. Control characters and special "escape sequences" are not required or used by CLOVER-2000. Compressed or encrypted data may therefore be sent without the need to insert (and filter) additional control characters and without concern for data integrity.

3. SIGNAL CHARACTERISTICS

Five different types of modulation may be used in the ARQ mode - BPSM (Binary Phase Shift Modulation), QPSM (Quadrature PSM), 8PSM (8-level PSM), 8P2A (8PSM + 2-level Amplitude Shift Modulation), and 16P4A (16 PSM plus 4 ASM). The same five types of modulation used in ARQ mode are also available in Broadcast (FEC) mode, with the addition of 2-Channel Diversity BPSM (2DPSM). Each CCB is sent using 2DPSM modulation, 17 byte block size, and 60% bias.

DATA THROUGHPUT
in bits per second (bps)

BIAS (Error Corrector Efficiency)

| Modulation | Robust (60%) | | Normal (75%) | Fast (90%) |
	FEC Mode (bps)	ARQ Mode (bps)	ARQ Mode (bps)	ARQ Mode (bps)
16P4A	1334	1323.5	1658.8	1994.1
8P2A	905	882.4	1105.9	1329.4
8PSM	741	661.8	829.4	997.1
QPSM	427	441.2	552.9	664.7
BPSM	224	220.6	276.5	332.4
(FEC only) 2DPSM	108	—	—	—

The maximum ARQ data throughput varies from 336 bits per second for BPSM to 1992 bits per second for 1 6P4A modulation. BPSM is most useful for weak and badly distorted data signals while the highest format (16P4A) needs extremely good channels, with high SNRs and almost no multipath.

4. HARDWARE IMPLEMENTATONS

Two different CLOVER-2000 modems are available from HAL Communications, the PCI-4000/2K and the DSP-4100/2K. The PCI-4000/2K is for use inside dedicated desk-top personal computers. The PCI-4000/2K may be installed in any IBM-compatible personal computer that uses an 80386 or faster microprocessor (386, 486, Pentium, etc.) and supports the ISA PC plug-in card bus. The DSP-4100/2K is for connection to lap-top or non-IBM-PC data systems. The DSP-4100/2K is a stand-alone DSP modem that may be used with any computer or data terminal equipment having an RS-232 port.

5. BI-DIRECTIONAL ARQ

Most ARQ protocols designed for use with HF radio systems can send data in only one direction at a time. For example, when using CCIR-476/625 (SITOR) or PACTOR, one station sends all of its data, ending the transmission with an "OVER" command. The second station may then send its information. Because CLOVER-2000 does not need an "OVER" command, data may flow in either direction at any time. The CLOVER ARQ time frame automatically adjusts to match the data volume to be sent in either or both directions. When first linked, both sides of the ARQ link exchange information using six bytes of the CCB. When one station has a large volume of data buffered and ready to send, ARQ mode automatically shifts to an expanded time frame during which one or more 255 byte data blocks are sent. If the second station also has a large volume of data buffered and ready to send, its half of the ARQ frame is also expanded. Either or both stations will shift back to CCB level when all buffered data has been sent. This feature provides the benefit of full-duplex data transfer but requires use of only simplex frequencies and half-duplex radio equipment. This two-way feature of CLOVER can also provide a back-channel order-wire capability. Communications may be maintained in this "chat" mode at 55 words per minute, which is more than adequate for real-time keyboard-to-keyboard communications.

6. BINARY FILE TRANSFER USING CLOVER-2000

The effective data throughput rate of CLOVER-2000 can be even higher when binary file transfer mode is used with data compression. The binary file transfer protocol used by HAL Communications operates with a terminal program explained in the HAL E2004 Engineering Document listed under References. Data compression algorithms tend to be context sensitive-compression that works well for one mode (e.g. text), may not work well for other data forms (graphics, etc.). The HAL terminal program uses the PK-WARE compression algorithm which has been proven to be a good general-purpose compressor for most computer files and programs. Other algorithms may be much more efficient for some data formats, particularly for compression of graphic image files and digitized voice data. The HAL Communications PCI-4000/2K and DSP-4100/2K modems can be operated with other data compression algorithms in the users' computers.

CLOVER 2000 REFERENCES

HAL Communications: "CLOVER-2000 High Performance Protocol," **www. halcomm.com/clvr2k**.

HAL Communications: "Binary File Transfer Protocol," E2004, Rev. B, HAL Communications Corp., Urbana, IL, December 1997.

HAL Communications: "CLOVER-2000 Waveform & Protocol," E2007, Rev. C, HAL Communications Corp., Urbana, IL, May 1999.

Wickwire, Ken, Mike Bernock and Bob Levreault, "On-air Measurements of CLOVER II and CLOVER 2000 Throughput," *Proc. 17th ARRL/TAPR Digital Communications Conference*, ARRL, Newington, CT, 1998, pp. 120-130.

G-TOR

1. PROTOCOL

G-TOR* (Golay-Teleprinting Over Radio) can be viewed, in part, as a variant of the Automatic Link Establishment (ALE) protocol, outlined in MIL-STD-188-141 A. G-TOR combines the error correcting properties of ALE, including Forward Error Correction (FEC) coding and full-frame interleaving, the Automatic Repeat reQuest (ARQ) cycle of Packet and a new application of the invertibility of the Golay code, to produce a faster new mode.

2. DATA FRAME STRUCTURE

G-TOR is a synchronous transmission system with a data frame duration of 1.92 seconds and a 0.48-second window between data fraines, for a total cycle time of 2.40 seconds regardless of transmission rate. Data frames are 192, 384, or 576 bits long sent at 100, 200, or 300 symbols/sec, respectively, with the data rate dependent on band conditions. Each data frame consists of a Data field and Status byte, followed by a two-byte Cyclic Redundancy Check (CRC). No start or ending flags are added to any of the frames, thus lowering overhead and resulting in improved frame efficiency relative to AMTOR and PacTOR. The Data field contains 21, 45, or 69 eight-bit bytes sent at 100, 200, or 300 symbols/sec, respectively. The Status byte provides the frame number identification, data format (whether standard 8-bit ASCII or Huffman compressed), and a command (data, turnaround request, disconnect, or connect) for a total of 8 bits.

*G-TOR is a trademark of Kantronics, Inc.

3. ACKNOWLEDGEMENT (ACK) FRAME STRUCTURE

ACK frames are used to acknowledge correct or incorrect receipt of data frames, to request changes in transmission speed, and to change the direction of information flow. There are five different ACK frames: Data frame received without error (send next frame), Data frame error detected, Speed-up, Speed-down, and Changeover. Each of the ACK frames consists of two eight-bit bytes sent from the information-receiving station to the information- sending station at 100 symbols/sec, for a duration of 0.16-second during the 0.48-second window between data frames. The Changeover ACK frame initiates a changeover in information flow direction by starting out with a two-byte Changeover ACK (which causes the information-sending station to stop sending) followed by 19 data bytes, a single status byte, and a two-byte CRC, for a duration of 1.92 seconds (the same as a data frame). None of the ACK frames are interleaved; however, each is generated from a set of pseudorandom numbers and up to three bit-errors are allowed per ACK, thus reducing needless retransmissions from faulty ACK signals. Hence the ACKs are called fuzzy. Link quality, denoted by a set number of consecutive good or bad frames, determines link speed.

4. ASCII CHARACTERS AND HUFFMAN / RUN-LENGTH COMPRESSION

G-TOR frames are sent in normal ASCII or are Huffman and run-length encoded, depending upon which is more efficient on a frame-by-frame basis. The Huffman table for G-TOR is unique: It differs from the PacTOR table in that it emphasizes English over German character usage and upper and lower case characters are swapped automatically (frame-by-frame) in a third attempt to compress data—hence Huffman forms A and B.

5. GOLAY ERROR-CORRECTION CODING AND INTERLEAVING

G-TOR uses extended Golay coding which is capable of correcting three or fewer errors in a received 24-bit code word. The Golay code used in G-TOR is a half-rate code, so that the encoder generates one error-correction bit (a parity bit) for every data transmitted. Interleaving is also used to correct burst errors which often occur from lightning, other noise, or interference. Interleaving is the last operation performed on the frame before transmission and de-interleaving is the first operation performed upon reception. Interleaving rearranges the bits in the frame so that long error bursts can be randomized when the de-interleaving is performed. When operating at 300 symbols/second, the interleaver reads 12-bit words into registers by columns and reads 48-bit words out of the registers by rows. The de-interleaver performs the inverse, reading the received data bits into registers by rows and extracting the original data sequence by reading the columns. A long burst of errors, for example 12-bits in duration, will be distributed into 48 separate 12-bit words before the error correction process is applied. This effectively nullifies the errors. Both data frames and parity frames are completely interleaved. In addition, by using the invertibility characteristic of Golay code words, data frames are always alternated with data frames coded in Golay parity bits. In this way, G-TOR can maintain full speed (when band conditions are good)—rather than fall to rate-1/2. Receiving parity bits can be used as data or as parity.

6. LINK INITIALIZATION

To establish a link, the information-sending station transmits the call sign of the intended receiver. Once the information-receiving station has synchronized, it sends an ACK to the information-sending station and data transmission begins.

7. SIGNAL CHARACTERISTICS

G-TOR uses frequency-shift keying like PacTOR and packet radio. At 300 symbols/second, and with the recommended frequency shift of 170 or 200 Hz, G-TOR's spectral characteristics are almost identical to those of packet radio.

8. ERROR DETECTION AND ARQ CYCLE

G-TOR provides error correction by using a combination of both ARQ retransmission and forward error-correction. The error-detection code transmitted with each frame is a 2-byte CRC code, the same used in the AX.25 packet protocol, and it is used to determine if the frame was received correctly before error correction is initiated and after error correction is completed, to ensure that the error-correction process has successfully removed all errors in the packet. Although the CRC error-detection code is used on every frame to detect errors, the Golay error-correction procedure is skipped unless errors are detected. This ability to skip unnecessary error correction is extremely valuable since forward error correction is very costly in terms of throughput. The Golay code used in G-TOR is a half-rate code, with one error-correction bit required for every information bit; however, by using the invertibility of the extended Golay code, the half-rate transmission result normally encountered with FEC systems is avoided. Frames made up of parity bits can be fully converted to data frames. Received frames are synchronized, deinterleaved, decoded and checked for proper CRC. If the frame is found to be in error, the information-receiving station will request that the matching parity frame be sent. If the parity (or data) frame that follows is found to be correct, that frame is acknowledged. If, however, it too is in error, it is combined with the previous data (or parity) frame in an attempt to recover the original data bits. In this way the system has three chances to recover the original data from the transmission of one data and one parity frame. If unsuccessful, the ARQ cycle begins again. The dispersal of noise-burst errors via interleaving, combined with the power of the Golay code to correct 3 bits in every 24, usually results in the recovery of error-free frames.

G-TOR REFERENCES

Anderson, Phil: "G-TOR's Evolutionary Improvements!" Kantronics Inc., Lawrence, KS, 1994.

Anderson, Phil: "H F ARQ Protocols," *RTTY Digital Journal*, April 1994.

Anderson, Phil, and Glenn Prescott: "Error-Correcting Codes," *RTTY Digital Journal*, March 1994.

Anderson, Phil, Michael Huslig, Glenn Prescott, and Karl Medcalf: "G-TOR: The New, Faster HIF Digital Mode for the KAM Plus," *RTTY Digital Journal*, March 1994, pp.1-2.

Ford, Steve: "G-TOR vs. PacTOR vs. AMTOR: A Nonscientific Throughput Test," *QEX*, American Radio Relay League, Newington, CT, May 1994, p. 18.

Kantronics: "G-TOR: The New HF Digital Mode for the KAM Plus and KAM Enhancement Board," Kantronics Inc., Lawrence, KS, 1994.

Karn, Phil: "Toward New Link-Layer Protocols," *QEX*, American Radio Relay League, Newington, CT, June 1994, pp. 3-10.

Prescott, Glenn, Phil Anderson, Mike Huslig, and Karl Medcalf: "G-TOR: A Hybrid ARQ Protocol for Narrow Bandwidth HF Data Communication," *QEX*, American Radio Relay League, Newington, CT, May 1994, pp. 12-19.

MFSK

1. INTRODUCTION

MFSK is an easy-to-use chat mode for real-time amateur contacts, nets and bulletin transmissions, but not intended for contesting or Bulletin Board System (BBS) use. It is a half-duplex non-Automatic Repeat ReQuest (ARQ) forward-error-correcting (FEC) mode. It performs well on long-path fading conditions and in the presence of interference. No special equipment will be required to set up a station to operate this mode.

2. DESCRIPTION OF MODES

2.1 Choice of Modes

The choice of useful modes offered by the software is limited. Other modes offered will be sufficiently different in nature and application to be obvious to the non-technical user (for example PSK31 is a suitable alternative). The default mode, known as MFSK16..MFSK 9-9, offers comfortable typing speed and quick manual half-duplex end of over turnaround. Turnaround time will not exceed five seconds using the default mode. Typing speed is dependent on mode and FEC settings, and the turnaround time will scale with data-rate changes and increase with addition of FEC. The default mode is 16-FSK, 16-tone, 15.625-baud transmission rate with FEC ON, Interleaver ON. The FEC will be R=1/2 K=7, using the NASA algorithms.

2.2 Mode Selection

The user software will automatically select number of tones, signaling rate, FEC and interleaver regimes from a single menu selection, invisible to the user. The user will not be able to change any of these parameters, nor will they be shown what the settings are. Different modes with clearly different performance will be provided only from a limited list, which descriptively names the modes.

3. TRANSMISSION TECHNIQUE

3.1. MFSK Technique

The transmission is based on 16-FSK (sequential single tone FSK), with continuous phase (CPSK) tones. There is no delay between tones, and no shaping of the tones.

3.2 Transmission Bandwidth

Transmission bandwidth will be less than the number of tones × tone spacing × 2 at the —30 dB point relative to a single carrier when properly adjusted. The transmitter does not need to be linear. Note that this is outside the second sidelobe, so should be easily achievable. The CCIR requirement is for less than 0.005% of the total power to be outside the necessary bandwidth, which is 316 Hz for the default mode 16FSK16. The ITU emission designator is 316HJ21B when produced by audio modulation of an SSB-SC transmitter.

3.3 Symbol Rate and Tone Spacing

The system uses a tone spacing numerically equal to the symbol rate. Each symbol consists of a single square keyed pulse with the same start and finish phase as all others, and concatenated with others. No single or isolated pulses, or gaps between pulses are emitted.

3.4 Range of Tones

Transmission tones (and receiver tuning) should be adjustable to suit different transceiver IF filters. Low (~1 kHz) and high (~2 kHz) alternatives to be accommodated without change of actual tone spacing.

3.5 Bit-Stream Orientation

At the lowest level, i.e. the single symbol, the system will be a bit-stream oriented transmission, allowing convolutional-code FEC, Varicode and binary transfer options to be used at a higher level. This approach allows maximum flexibility; for example, it also allows data block transmission over sequential tones, such as is used in Piccolo, with two sequential tones per character.

3.6 FEC Coding

Full-time FEC coding with interleaver is used with this mode. FEC is sequential R=1/2, K=7, using NASA algorithms. The interleaver will be self-synchronizing, based on 10 concatenated 4 × 4 bit IZ8BLY diagonal interleavers.

3.7 Alphabet Coding

The default alphabet coding will be the IZ8BLY Varicode, using an extended ASCII character set and super-ASCII control codes.

3.8 Idle Limitation

To avoid extended periods of single tone (for example, when the keyboard buffer is empty), a non-printing character is stuffed periodically into the transmit system as though it came from the keyboard. A non-printing character is sent whenever the transmitter is idle for 20 symbol periods. Stuffing will not occur when the buffer is not empty. Idle will be achieved by sending ASCII NULL or other non-printing character, followed by an extended zero bit stream, e.g., "0000000000000000." The latter will be rejected by the receiver as an invalid character.

Comment: It is intended in future releases of this specification to describe a "secondary data channel." Special characters for secondary channel data, which will be outside the extended ASCII character set defined in paragraph C.10, will allow transmission of low priority data during idle, exactly like the IZ8BLY MT63 "secondary channel." The data rate would be very low, but would permit automatic ID. These super-ASCII characters would be used in place of the above mentioned NULL character. The purpose of the "diddle" is to allow the receiver symbol clock to remain in lock. The diddle must not be continuous, as the idle period is used for signal tuning purposes.

3.9 Beginning and End of Transmission

At the start of transmission an idle carrier representing the lowest tone is transmitted for 8 symbol periods. At end of transmission all pending transmit characters is sent, and the transmitter is flushed with zeros, allowing an idle period of at least 4 symbol periods to be transmitted. The purpose of the idle carrier is to allow accurate manual tuning.

3.10 Tone Bit Weighting

Tone weighting is such that the lowest audio tone represents zeros in all bits. The weighting will increase in gray-code as the tone frequency is increased. This technique provides the least Hamming.MFSK 9-11 distance between adjacent tones:

Tone	Weight	Tone	Weight
0 (lowest)	0000	8	1100
1	0001	9	1101
2	0011	10	1111
3	0010	11	1110
4	0110	12	1010
5	0111	13	1011
6	0101	14	1001
7	0100	15	1000 (highest)

4. THE RECEIVER

4.1 Demodulator Technique

The receiver uses non-coherent demodulation, employing an FFT filter and demodulator technique, integrating the signal over the symbol tone period by sampling the period synchronously with the transmitted symbol. A recovered symbol clock will be used to accomplish this purpose. Reduction of multi-path reception effects can be achieved by windowing the symbol sample period to exclude, for example, the first and last 5 ms worth of samples.

4.2 Decision Decoding

The symbol decision decoder which follows the FFT will preferably use bit-wise soft decisions. The symbol decision decoder may offer soft decisions to the FEC decoder.

4.3 Tuning Indicators and AFC

The symbol decision decoder provides tuning indication, as well as signal performance metering (S/N meter). Automatic Frequency Control may be offered. This mode will be very sensitive, and very narrow, so will require very accurate tuning. Due consideration needs to be given to accurately tuning almost inaudible signals, through use of a good expanded waterfall display.

A S/N meter in arbitrary units based on data from the symbol decision decoder will be useful. AGC is not required with an FFT approach.

4.4 FEC Decoding

The FEC decoder uses soft decisions, and may use soft data from the symbol decoder. The FEC regime can identify the FEC dibits unambiguously from the fixed weight bits in the received symbols.

4.5 Confidence Meter

The FEC decoder may provide information for a "signal confidence" meter, which reflects the current reliability of FEC decoding from the decoder metrics.

4.6 Default Text Mode

The default receiver text mode uses a specially adapted Varicode, translating into ASCII for display. Characters outside the defined extended ASCII character set is not be displayed, i.e., will not be sent to the screen. This use of non-printing special characters permits these characters to provide symbol sync or carry a secondary channel text thread where supported by the software, without requiring support to be part of these specifications.

4.7 Other Requirements

4.7.1 Symbol Sync

Receiver symbol synchronization will be affected by using transmitted carrier phase or data transition information or by multiple FEC decoder voting, rather than recovering AM modulation, since the transmitter is hard keyed. (The original Piccolo used AM modulation of tones to transmit sync. MFSK16 does not, but transmits constant-phase carriers. CPFSK transmissions make these techniques possible.)

4.7.2 Symbol Clock

The received symbol phase will remain substantially correct (within 90 degrees) for at least 50 symbol clock periods while receiving an idle condition, and will retain phase with one non-printing character every 20 symbols.

4.7.3 Tuning Display and Tuning

The user interface provides a waterfall tuning display, preferably with point and click tuning, but with at least easy tuning in steps of 1/4 of the tone spacing or better.

4.7.4 User Interface Windows

The user interface provides separate TX and RX windows, a type-ahead buffer and simple macros.

4.7.5 Identification and Tuning Signal

Morse ID and a transmitter tuning signal are provided. Suggestion: OOK of the lowest tone, or FSK between lowest and highest tones would be suitable for the ID, as it would assist receiver tuning. Transmitter idle will suffice for the tuning signal.

4.7.6 USB/LSB Reverse Switch

A reverse switch may be provided to allow copy of wrong-sideband signals. If provided, the transmitter will reverse in concert with the receiver.

5. DOCUMENTATION

5.1 Software Copyright

User software (released binaries) of software offering this mode will be copyright of the author, and all rights will be retained by the various authors. All source code copyright to be retained by the author. All source code must be submitted to the MFSK development team if the software claims to be written to this specification. The development team "committee" will review all source and executables before approval is given. Submitted source code will not be published without the authors' permission, but if the software is approved will be retained and offered to interested developers on request. Permission to use the MFSK16 logo will be provided for incorporation into approved software.

5.2 Non-Amateur Use

Commercial or military use of the released binaries will be permitted only as agreed by the contributing authors and owner of this specification. No responsibility for damages or lack of performance is assumed by the owner, the authors, or any of the development team. (The purposes of this paragraph are to (a) discourage commercial exploitation of the product or concept without approval and involvement of the developers; and (b) to protect the developers from unreasonable demands.)

5.3 Publication of Specifications

Algorithms and code tables sufficient to define the mode will be published as electronic documents, are referred to and referenced in this document. The documents will be retained on the MFSK Web site at **www.qsl.net/zl1bpu/MFSK**. A reference version of the source code will be made available to interested developers. These released documents, along with this specification, will constitute the complete description of the mode.

5.4 User Documentation

Software developers are to make their own arrangements for documentation of their software. Installation and operating information will accompany each release.

5.5 Release of Non-compliant Software

No user software will be released which purports to support this specification but which offers for public use MFSK operation not covered by this specification. This particularly applies to test versions and beta versions. Test features in these releases must be protected from public access.

5.6 Freeware Availability

All user software (released binaries) will be made available free of charge, other than media costs, perhaps via an end-user license. The software will be fully operational and fully documented.

6. ACKNOWLEDGEMENT

The information was based on a description prepared by Murray Greenman, ZL1BPU.

PACTOR

1. PROTOCOL

PACTOR can be viewed as a combination of two earlier digital modes, packet radio and AMateur Teleprinting Over Radio (AMTOR). PACTOR provides improved throughput because its transmission speed adapts to the quality of the link and it uses Huffman compressed characters. PACTOR operates over half-duplex links and uses an Automatic Repeat reQuest (ARQ) protocol, acknowledging each individual data packet with a short Control Signal (CS). Some PACTOR implementations provide a Memory-ARQ feature to determine and store the relative strength of each received bit. Copies of corrupted frames stored this way are correlated with frames received later, to provide a coding gain for improved error correction.

2. PACKET LENGTH AND ACKNOWLEDGMENT

PACTOR is a synchronous transmission system with a packet duration of 0.96 second, a CS duration of 0.12 second, and an idle time of 0.17 second for a total cycle time of 1.25 seconds. The idle time is required for turaround procedures and settling, which allows for a maximum distance of about 20,000 km as in AMTOR. Clock reference is crystal controlled with an internal standard to at least 15×10^{-6} accuracy. The initiating station is the Master, and the other station is the Slave. PACTOR subjects each received packet to a Cyclic Redundancy Check (CRC) which triggers an ARQ for packets failing the CRC. The receiving station provides acknowledgment by sending a CS. Repetition of the same CS indicates a request for a packet to be repeated. The CS has a standard length of 12 bits and is always sent at 100 bauds.

3. PACKET COMPOSITION AND BAUD RATE

Packets are either 96 bits long sent at 100 bauds or 192 bits long sent at 200 bauds, with the data rate dependent on conditions. Each packet consists of a Header byte, Data field, and Status byte, followed by the

CRC byte given twice. The Header byte consists of the 8-bit pattern for 55 hexadecimal and is used for synchronization, MemoryARQ, and listen mode. The Data field contains 64 bits if sent at 100 bauds or 160 bits if sent at 200 bauds. Its format is normally Huffman-compressed ASCII, with conventional 8-bit ASCII as the alternative. The Status byte provides the packet count, data format (whether standard 8-bit ASCII or Huffman-compressed ASCII), break-in request, and QRT bit, for a total of 8 bits. The CRC calculation is based on the ITU-T polynomial $xE16+xE12+xE5+1$. The CRC byte is calculated for the whole packet starting with the data field, without Header, and consists of 16 bits. There are four different Control Signals, identified as CS1, CS2, CS3, and CS4, the functions of which are explained below.

4. LINK INITIALIZATION

To initiate a PACTOR connection, the Master station sends a special synchronization packet which contains the standard Header byte followed by the call sign (address) of the Slave station in both a 100-baud and a 200-baud bit pattern. (Each address field allows for up to eight characters, with the character 0F hexadecimal following the call sign in each unused space.) This allows the 200-baud bit pattern to determine the quality of the channel: The Slave responds with CS1 (4D5 hexadecimal) if the 200-baud bit pattern was received without error, or CS4 (D2C hexadecimal) if not, which leads to an instant reduction of data rate to 100 bands. After receiving the first CS1 or CS4 from the Slave, the Master sends the first data packet with Header=AA hexadecimal and packet count=1. System specific data, including the Master call sign, is sent automatically at the beginning. If the Slave is busy, it can both acknowledge and reject a connection by sending one CS2 (AB2 hexadecimal) each time it receives a correct synchronization pattern. The Master terminates its connect request after receiving CS2 twice in succession.

5. CHANGING SPEED

The decision regarding a speed change is made at the receiving end, by automatically evaluating the data input rate and packet statistics including error rate and number of retries. The receiving station transmits CS1 (acknowledge) following each correctly received packet, or CS4 (speed change request) following receipt of a bad 200-baud packet. The data contained in each unacknowledged 200-baud packet is automatically repeated at 100 bauds. This repetition requires several 100-baud packets because of the smaller Data field. If the receiving station acknowledges a correctly received 100-baud packet with CS4, the transmitting station sends the next packet at 200 bauds. If the following 200-baud packet is not acknowledged after an operator-selectable number of attempts (normally two), the speed is automatically set back to 100 bauds.

6. CHANGING DIRECTION AND ENDING CONNECTION

The receiving station can change to transmit by sending CS3 (3413 hexadecimal) as a break-in request at the head of its first data packet. At the end of a connection, special end of contact (QRT) synchronization packets are transmitted which contain the receiver address in the reversed order. This process is repeated until the sending station has received the acknowledgement.

7. ASCII CHARACTERS AND HUFFMAN COMPRESSION

PACTOR normally uses ASCII characters that have been compressed with a Huffman algorithm. This Huffman compression reduces the average character length for improved efficiency. The Annex shows the Huffman compressed equivalent of each ASCII character used in PACTOR, with the least significant bit (LSB) given first. The length of individual characters varies from 2 to 15 bits, with the most frequently used characters being the shortest. This results in an average character length of 4 to 5 bits for English text, instead of the 8 bits required for normal ASCII.

8. SIGNAL CHARACTERISTICS

PACTOR uses frequency-shift keying (FSK). With the recommended frequency shift of 200 Hz, PACTOR can be received through a filter with a bandwidth as narrow as 600 Hz.

PACTOR REFERENCES

Helfert, Hans-Peter, and Ulrich Strate: "PacTOR Radioteletype with Memory ARQ and Data Compression," *QEX*, American Radio Relay League, Newington, CT, October 1991, pp. 3-6.

Horzepa, Stan: "PacTOR: Better HF Data Communications for the Rest of Us?", *QST*, American Radio Relay League, Newington, CT, February 1993, p. 98.

Rogers, Buck: "PacTOR - The New Frontier," *CQ*, CQ Communications, Hicksville, NY, July 1993, pp. 88-95.

Van Der Westhuizen, Mike: "A Practical Comparison Between Clover and Pactor Data Transfer Rates," *CQ*, CQ Communications, Hicksville, NY, February 1994, pp. 40-42.

PACTOR Huffman Compression

Char	ASCII	Huffman (LSB [sent first] on left)
space	32	10
e	101	011
n	10	0101
i	105	1101
r	114	1110
t	116	00000
s	115	00100
d	100	00111
a	97	01000
u	117	11111
l	108	000010
h	104	000100
g	103	000111
m	109	001011
<CR>	13	001100
<LF>	10	001101
o	111	010010
c	99	010011
b	98	0000110
f	102	0000111
w	119	0001100
D	68	0001101
k	107	0010101
z	122	1100010
.	46	1100100
,	44	1100101
S	83	1111011
A	65	00101001
E	69	11000000
P	112	11000010
v	118	11000011
O	48	11000111
F	70	11001100
B	66	11001111
C	67	11110001
I	73	11110010
T	84	11110100
O	79	000101000
P	80	000101100
1	49	001010000
R	82	110000010
(	40	110011011
)	41	110011100
L	76	110011101
N	78	111100000
Z	90	111100110
M	77	111101010
9	57	0001010010

Char	ASCII	Huffman (LSB [sent first] on left)
W	87	0001010100
5	53	0001010101
y	121	0001010110
2	50	0001011010
3	51	0001011011
4	52	0001011100
6	54	0001011101
7	55	0001011110
8	56	0001011111
H	72	0010100010
J	74	1100000110
U	85	1100000111
V	86	1100011000
<FS>	28	1100011001
x	120	1100011010
K	75	1100110100
?	63	1100110101
=	61	1111000010
q	113	1111010110
Q	81	1111010111
j	106	00010100110
G	71	00010100111
-	45	00010101111
:	58	00101000111
!	33	11110011101
/	47	11110011110
*	42	001010001100
"	34	110001101100
%	37	110001101101
'	39	110001101110
_	95	111100001100
&	38	111100111001
+	43	111100111110
>	62	111100111111
@	64	0001010111000
$	36	0001010111001
<	60	0001010111010
X	88	0001010111011
#	35	0010100011011
Y	89	00101000110101
;	59	11110000110100
\	92	11110000110101
[	91	001010001101000
]	93	001010001101000
<DEL>	127	110001101111000
~	126	110001101111001
}	125	110001101111010
|	124	110001101111011
{	123	110001101111100
'	96	110001101111101

Char	ASCII	Huffman (LSB [sent first] on left)
^	94	110001101111110
<US>	31	110001101111111
<GS>	29	111100001101100
<ESC>	27	111100001101101
<EM>	25	111100001101110
<CAN>	24	111100001101111
<ETB>	23	111100001110000
<SYN>	22	111100001110001
<NAK>	21	111100001110010
<DC4>	20	111100001110011
<DC3>	19	111100001110100
<DC2>	18	111100001110101
<DC1>	17	111100001110110
<DLE>	16	111100001110111
<RS>	30	111100001111000
<SI>	15	111100001111001
<SO>	14	111100001111010
<FF>	12	111100001111011
<VT>	11	111100001111100
<HT>	9	111100001111101
<BS>	8	111100001111110
<BEL>	7	111100001111111
<ACK>	6	111100111000000
<ENQ>	5	111100111000001
<EOT>	4	111100111000010
<ETX>	3	111100111000011
<STX>	2	111100111000100
<SOH>	1	111100111000101
<NUL>	0	111100111000110
<SUB>	26	111100111000111

PACTOR II

1. INTRODUCTION

PACTOR II is a fully backward-compatible improvement to the original PACTOR system. It is an adaptive mode that applies different modulation and encoding methods depending on the channel quality. PACTOR II performs its initial link setup using PACTOR in order to achieve compatibility. An automatic handover to PACTOR II is made only if both stations are capable of PACTOR operation. While PACTOR uses frequency-shift keying (FSK) modulation, PACTOR II uses two-tone differential phase-shift keying (DPSK) modulation.

PACTOR II's highest data transfer rate without compression is 700 bit/s under optimum conditions, which can provide a maximum effective throughput of up to 1200 bit/s (for text with real-time data compression enabled). PACTOR

II's improved error control coding enables it to operate on circuits with (S+N)/ N ratios as much as 7 dB lower than PACTOR can tolerate.

2. STRUCTURE AND TIMING OF PACTOR II FRAMES

Similar to PACTOR, PACTOR II is also a half-duplex protocol that uses Automatic Repeat reQuest (ARQ) to acknowledge each individual data packet with a short control signal (CS). An "over" must be inserted into the data stream to change direction. The basic PACTOR 11 frame structure consists of a header, a variable data field, a status byte and a cyclic redundancy check (CRC). The standard cycle duration for PACTOR II is the same 1.25 s used by PACTOR, with the same 0.17s idle time (for propagation delay), to maintain interoperability. Since PACTOR II uses a longer CS of 0.28 s (instead of PACTOR's 0.12 s), the packet length had to be shortened to 0.8 s (from PACTOR's 0.96 s). The transceiver requirements for transmit delay and receiver recovery time therefore remain the same for PACTOR II as they are for PACTOR.

PACTOR II uses six different CSs, each consisting of 40 bits. As in PACTOR, CS1 and CS2 are used to acknowledge/request packets and CS3 forces a break-in. CS4 and CS5 handle the speed changes, and CS6 is a toggle for the packet length.

Due to the signal propagation delay and equipment switching delays PACTOR II has a maximum range for ARQ contacts of approximately 20,000 km. As with PACTOR, a long-path option is available to enable contacts up to 40,000 km. The sending station must call the receiving station in "long-path" mode. Initial contact is established using the ordinary PACTOR protocol, but with a cycle time of 1.4 s instead of 1.25 s. This longer cycle time allows for the much greater propagation delays found on long-path contacts. The link then automatically switches to PACTOR II, with the same cycle duration. A switch between "normal" and "long-path" modes requires ending the link and reconnecting. In the new "data mode" (see below), timing is also automatically adjusted to obtain longer receiving gaps.

Unlike PACTOR, PACTOR II automatically switches to longer packets if the data blocks are not filled up with idles; i.e., if the transmitter buffer indicates that more information has to be transferred than fits into the standard packets. If the information sending station (ISS) prefers to use long packets, it sets the long-cycle flag in the status word. The PACTOR II information receiving station (IRS) then finally can accept the proposed change of the cycle duration by sending a CS6. This situation, for example, occurs when reading longer files out of mailboxes. The long packets are basically made up like the short ones, but consist of a larger data field that may contain up to 2208 bits of usable information. The length of these data packets is 3.28 s, which leads to an entire cycle duration of 3.75 s in this "data mode."

3. ERROR CONTROL CODING

Effective transmission of data over difficult HF paths requires substantial error control coding (ECC). Full frame interleaving is required for cancelling out error bursts and short fading periods, especially with the longer data packets being used. PACTOR II uses a convolutional code with a constraint length of 9, a real Viterbi decoder, and soft decision. Due to the high coding gain and resulting capacity of error correction without requesting a repetition of the entire packet, a significant increase in the effective throughput can usually be attained.

ECC requires redundant bits be appended to the data before transmission through a noisy channel. The redundant bits are generated from the original data by applying special rules that depend on the chosen code. The ratio of the number of information bits to the whole length is the code rate.

Two main approaches of ECC can be distinguished: block codes and convolutional codes. Convolutional codes require data interleaving to be effective on channels with burst errors from noise or interference. When applying block codes (such as Golay, Hamming and Reed-Solomon), the message or packet is divided into data blocks. Each block is then encoded separately and forms a code word. Block codes can easily be implemented as they often show a cyclic property and may not require much processing power. Block codes do not require interleaving because of their tolerance for burst errors, thus are efficient for use over HF radio.

Convolutional codes encode the entire message packet and the resulting code words are longer than the original packet. The complexity of a convolutional code mainly depends on the number of tapped shift registers, which work as binary convolvers, and represent the heart of the convolutional encoder. The eight shift registers used in PACTOR II provide a constraint length of 9. This sets the upper boundary for the achievable coding gain. PACTOR II uses a Viterbi decoder with soft decision to implement maximum likelihood decoding.

PACTOR II uses a rate 1/2 convolutional code. Code with higher rates, e.g., rate 2/3 and rate 7/8, are derived by a process called "puncturing." Prior to their transmission, certain of the symbols of the rate 1/2 encoded stream are punctured or deleted and not transmitted. At the receiving end, the punctured encoded bits are replaced with "null" symbols prior to decoding with the rate 1/2 decoder. The decoder treats these null symbols neither as a received "1" nor "0" but as an exactly intermediate value. No information is thus conveyed by that symbol that may influence the decoding process. The major advantage of this approach is that a single code rate decoder (in this case a rate 1/2 decoder) can implement a wide range of codes. In PACTOR II, the Viterbi algorithm is implemented for decoding the convolutional code.

PACTOR II provides a more robust Listen Mode than PACTOR because just the short header has to be received correctly to enable use of the ECC. Burst errors may be corrected by monitoring stations. The same speed and encoding levels used by PACTOR II are also available in its Unproto Mode. On the receiving side, the correct mode is detected automatically.

4. MODULATION

PACTOR II uses various DPSK modulation schemes and different code rates, depending on conditions. Differential binary phase-shift keying (DBPSK) is the most robust modulation used by PACTOR II, so it is used for sending all control signals. If propagation conditions improve, PACTOR II automatically switches to differential quadrature phase-shift keying (DQPSK) modulation. If conditions improve further, it changes to 8-DPSK and finally to 16DPSK under optimum conditions.

A single-tone 100 bit/s DBPSK signal can transfer 100 bit/s. PACTOR II uses two-tone DBPSK modulation in its most robust mode, which can be thought of as two single-tone DBPSK signals used together, resulting in a data rate 200 bit/s. This data rate is lowered by the redundancy required in the coding to reduce the error rate, so that the effective throughput becomes 100 bit/s with rate 1/2 coding.

PACTOR II uses different forms of two-tone DPSK modulation in all of its modes and starts using DBPSK modulation at a data rate of 200 bit/s with rate 1/2 coding to provide a throughput of 100 bit/s. The next step uses DQPSK modulation at a data rate of 400 bit/s also with rate 1/2 coding, for a throughput of 200 bit/s. This is followed by 8-DPSK modulation at a data rate of 600 bit/s with rate 2/3 coding, for a throughput of 400 bit/s. Finally, in the best propagation conditions, PACTOR II uses 16-DPSK modulation at 800 bit/s with a rate 7/8 coding, for a throughput of 700 bit/s. These throughputs are all the maximum uncompressed data transfer rates which are realised only if no packets need to be re-sent because of errors. PACTOR II automatically selects the modulation and hence the data rate by considering the error repeat history (although this is not a true link quality assessment). When data compression is active, the effective data transfer rates may be considerably higher.

5. ON-LINE DATA COMPRESSION

Both PACTOR and PACTOR II use an automatic online data compression algorithm that is optimised for text, starting with Huffman encoding. Additionally, PACTOR II uses run-length encoding and pseudo-Markov compression (PMC). Compared to 8-bit ASCII (plain text), PMC yields a compression factor of around 1.9. This leads to an effective speed of about 600 bit/s in average propagation conditions in data mode. PACTOR II is already around three times faster than PACTOR on average channels. However, the maximum effective speed in good conditions can reach 1200 bit/s. PACTOR II firmware automatically checks whether PMC, Huffman or the original ASCII code is the best choice. PACTOR II is also able to transfer and 7-bit ASCII data and other binary information (such as programs, pictures and voice files) which can be split up into 4-bit nibbles by automatically switching off its on-line data compression.

6. SIGNAL CHARACTERISTICS

Similar to PACTOR, the tones of the PACTOR II signal are spaced at 200 Hz. Their centre frequency may be defined in steps of 1 Hz, by software command, between 400 Hz and 2600 Hz, as long as the shift remains 200 Hz. In the PACTOR II system, the transferred information is swapped from one channel (tone) to the other in every cycle. This swapping provides resistance to strong narrowband interference (e.g., CW) which might completely overpower one channel, so the signal can still get transferred but at a reduced speed. PACTOR II signals can be received through filters as narrow as 500 Hz.

PACTOR-III

Technical Description

PACTOR-III is a software upgrade for existing PACTOR-II modems that provides a new data transmission mode for improved speed and robustness. PACTOR-III is not a new modem or hardware device. Most current PACTOR-II modems are upgradeable to use PACTOR-III via a software update since PACTOR-II firmware accommodates the new PACTOR-III software. Both the transmitting and receiving stations must support PACTOR-III for end-to-end communications using this mode.

PACTOR-III's maximum uncompressed speed is 2722 bps. Using online compression, up to 5.2 kbps is achievable. This requires an audio passband from 400 Hz to 2600 Hz (for PACTOR-III speedlevel 6). The occupied bandwidth at the –40 dB points is 2.4 kHz (from 300 Hz to 2700 Hz).

On an average channel, PACTOR-III is over three times faster than PACTOR-II. On good channels, the effective throughput ratio between PACTOR-III and PACTOR-II can exceed five. PACTOR-III is slightly more robust than PACTOR-II at their lower SNR edges.

The ITU emission designator for PACTOR-III is 2K20J2D. Because PACTOR-III builds on PACTOR-II, most specifications like frame length and frame structure are adopted from PACTOR-II. The only significant difference is PACTOR III's multi-tone waveform which uses up to 18 carriers while PACTOR-II uses only two carriers. PACTOR-III's carriers are located in a 120 Hz grid and modulated with 100 symbols per second DBPSK or DQPSK. Channel coding is also adopted from PACTOR-II's Punctured Convolutional Coding.

Link Establishment

The calling modem uses the PACTOR-I FSK connect frame for compatibility. When the called modem answers, the modems negotiate to the highest level of which both modems are capable. If one modem is only capable of PACTOR-II, then the 500 Hz PACTOR-II mode is used for the session. With the MYLevel command a user may limit a modem's highest mode. For example, a user may set MYL to "1" and only a PACTOR-I connection will be made, set to "2" and PACTOR-I and II connections are available, set to "3" and PACTOR-I through III connections are enabled. The default MYL is set to "2" with the current firmware and with PACTOR-III firmware it will be set to "3". If a user is only allowed to occupy a 500 Hz channel, MYL can be set to "2" and the modem stay in its PACTOR-II mode.

The PACTOR-III Protocol Specification is available on the Web at **www.scs-ptc.com/pactor.html**.

The possible sub-protocol levels used in PACTOR-III are called *speedlevels*. The carrier localization of the speedlevels is:

Carrier Number	0	1	2	3	4	5	6	7	8	9	0	1	2	3	4	5	6	7
Speedlevel																		
1						X							X					
2			X		X		X					X		X		X		
3			X	X	X	X	X	X	X	X	X	X	X	X	X			
4			X	X	X	X	X	X	X	X	X	X	X	X	X	X		
5		X	X	X	X	X	X	X	X	X	X	X	X	X	X	X		
6	X	X	X	X	X	X	X	X	X	X	X	X	X	X	X	X	X	X

A free trial version of PACTOR-III is downloadable from **www.scs-ptc.com**, but it operates for only 20 connections so a license must be obtained for permanent use.

Speedlevel	Number of tones	Code Rate	Modulation Type
1	2	1/2	DBPSK
2	6	1/2	DBPSK
3	14	1/2	DBPSK
4	14	1/2	DQPSK
5	16	3/4	DQPSK
6	18	8/9	DQPSK

PSK31

1. INTRODUCTION

PSK31 is a digital communications mode which is intended for live keyboard-to-keyboard conversations, similar to radioteletype. Its data rate is 31.25 baud (about 50 word-per-minute), and its narrow bandwidth (less than 80 Hz) reduces its susceptibility to noise. It uses BPSK modulation without error correction or QPSK modulation with error correction (convolutional encoding and Viterbi decoding). In order to eliminate splatter from the phase-reversals inherent to PSK, the output is cosine-filtered before reaching the transmitter audio input. PSK31 is readily monitored and the most popular implementation uses DSP software running on a computer soundcard inside an IBM PC-compatible computer.

There is a preamble at the start of each transmission and a postamble at the end. The preamble is an idle signal of continuous zeroes, corresponding to continuous phase reversals at the symbol rate of 31.25 reversals/second. The postamble is just continuous unmodulated carrier, representing a series of logical ones. This makes it possible to use the presence or absence of the reversals to "squelch" the decoder so that the screen doesn't fill with noise when there is no signal.

2. VARICODE CHARACTERS

Different characters are represented by a variable-length combination of bits called Varicode. Because shorter bit-lengths are used for the more common letters, Varicode improves efficiency in terms of the average character duration. Varicode is also self- synchronizing: No separate process is needed to define where one character ends and the next begins, since the pattern used to represent a gap between two characters (at least two consecutive zeroes) never occurs in a character. Because no Varicode characters can begin or end with a zero, the shortest character is a single one by itself. The next is 11, then 101, 111, 1011, and 1101, but not 10, 100, or 1000 (because they end with zeroes), and not 1001 (since it contains two consecutive zeros). This scheme generates the 128-character ASCII set with ten bits.

The Varicode character set is shown following, starting with NUL and ending with DEL. The codes are transmitted left bit first, with "0" representing a phase reversal on BPSK and "1" representing a steady carrier. A minimum of two zeros is inserted between characters. Some implementations may not handle all the codes below 32. Note that the lower case letters have the shortest patterns and so are the fastest to transmit.

The Varicode Character Set

NUL	1010101011	DLE	1011110111
SOH	1011011011	DCI	1011110101
STX	1011101101	DC2	1110101101
ETX	1101110111	DC3	1110101111
EOT	1011101011	DC4	1101011011
ENQ	1101011111	NAK	1101101011
ACK	1011101111	SYN	1101101101
BEL	1011111101	ETB	1101010111
BS	1011111111	CAN	1101111011
HT	11101111	EM	1101111101
LF	11101	SUB	1110110111
VT	1101101111	ESC	1101010101
FF	1011011101	FS	1101011101
CR	11111	GS	1110111011
SO	1101110101	RS	1011111011
SI	1110101011	US	1101111111
SP	1	C	10101101
!	111111111	D	10110101
"	101011111	E	1110111
#	111110101	F	11011011
$	111011011	G	11111101
%	1011010101	H	101010101
&	1010111011	I	1111111
'	101111111	J	111111101
(	11111011	K	101111101
)	11110111	L	11010111
*	101101111	M	10111011
+	111011111	N	11011101
,	1110101	O	10101011
-	110101	p	11010101
.	1010111	Q	111011101
/	110101111	R	10101111
0	10110111	S	1101111
1	10111101	T	1101101
2	11101101	U	101010111
3	11111111	V	110110101
4	101110111	X	101011101
5	101011011	Y	101110101
6	101101011	Z	101111011
7	110101101	[	1010101101
8	110101011	\	111110111
9	110110111	]	111101111
:	11110101	^	111111011
;	110111101	_	1010111111
<	111101101	.	101101101
=	1010101	/	1011011111

>	111010111	a	1011
?	1010101111	b	1011111
@	1010111101	c	101111
A	1111101	d	101101
B	11101011	e	11
f	111101	s	10111
g	1011011	t	101
h	101011	u	110111
i	1101	v	1111011
j	111101011	w	1101011
k	10111111	x	11011111
l	11011	y	1011101
m	111011	z	111010101
n	1111	{	1010110111
o	111	|	110111011
p	1111111	}	1010110101
q	110111111	~	1011010111
r	10101	' DEL	1110110101

3. QPSK MODE

The QPSK mode reduces the error-rate while keeping the bandwidth and the traffic speed the same. There is a 3-dB SNR penalty with QPSK, because the same transmitter power is being shared by twice the signals. Therefore, the error-correction scheme has to be at least good enough to correct the extra errors which result from the 3 dB SNR penalty, and preferably a lot more, or it will not be worth doing. By doing simulations in a computer, and tests on the bench with a noise generator, it has been found that when the bit error-rate is less than 1% with BPSK, it is much better than 1% with QPSK and error-reduction, but when the BER is worse than 1% on BPSK, the QPSK mode is actually worse than BPSK. Therefore, if we are dealing with radio paths where the signal is just simply very noisy, there is actually no advantage to QPSK at all!

On-the-air testing shows that QPSK with the convolutional coding for error-reduction is usually better than BPSK, except where the signal was deliberately attenuated to make it artificially weak. Typical radio circuits are far from being non-fading with white noise. Typical radio paths have errors in bursts rather than randomly spread, and error-reduction schemes can give useful benefits in this situation in a way that cannot be achieved by anything which can be done in the linear part of the signal path. With the convolutional coding used in PSK31, a 5:1 improvement is typical, but it does depend on the kind of path being used. There may be times when one mode works better than the other, and other times when the reverse will be the case. The switch between "straight" BPSK and "error-corrected" QPSK modes in PSK31 is done with both the bandwidth and the data-rate remaining the same. Contacts tend to start on BPSK and change to QPSK if both stations agree. Although both stations have to be using the same sideband in QPSK, it doesn't matter for BPSK.

4. CONVOLUTIONAL CODING

Convolutional coding is used to reduce errors in the QPSK mode. In a convolutional code, the characters are converted to a bitstream and then this bitstream is itself processed to add the error-reduction qualities. Since the convolutional code used in PSK31 doubles the number of data bits, it is a natural choice for the QPSK mode which provides double the bit-rate available with BPSK. The convolutional encoder generates one of the four phase-shifts, not from each data bit to be sent, but from a sequence of them. This means that each bit is effectively spread out in time, intertwined with earlier and later bits in a precise way. The more spread out, the better will be the ability of the code to correct bursts of noise, but too great a spread would introduce an excessive transmission delay. A time spread of 5 bits was chosen.

It is not quite correct to refer to the convolutional code system as "error-correcting" since the raw data is not actually transmitted in its original form and therefore it makes no sense to talk about it being corrupted by the link and corrected in the decoder. In PSK31, the raw data is transformed from binary (1 of 2) to quaternary (1 of 4) in such a way that there is a precisely known pattern in the sequence of quaternary symbols. In the code used in PSK31, each quaternary symbol transmitted is derived from a run of 5 consecutive data bits. This means that each binary bit to be transmitted generates a 5-symbol sequence, overlapping with the sequences from adjacent bits, in a predictable way which the receiver can use to estimate the correct sequence even in the presence of corruptions in parts of the sequence.

The Convolutional Code

The left columns in the following table contain the 32 combinations of a run of five Varicode bits, transmitted left bit first. The right columns are the corresponding phase shifts to be applied to the carrier, in degrees. A continuous phase advance is the same as an HF frequency shift.

00000	180	01000	0	10000	+90	11000	−90
00001	+90	01001	−90	10001	180	11001	0
00010	−90	01010	+90	10010	0	11010	180
00011	0	01011	180	10011	−90	11011	+90
00100	−90	01100	+90	10100	0	11100	180
00101	0	01101	180	10101	−90	11101	+90
00110	180	01110	0	10110	+90	11110	−90
00111	+90	01111	−90	10111	180	11111	0

For example, consider the "space" symbol—a single 1 preceded and followed by character gaps of five zeroes each: 00000 100000. Overlaying a five-bit-wide window on 00000100000, and sliding it from left to right (one bit at-a-time) is illustrated in the following table.

											Phase
0	0	0	0	0	1	0	0	0	0	0	Phase
0	0	0	0	0							180
	0	0	0	0	1						+90
		0	0	0	1	0					−90
			0	0	1	0	0				−90
				0	1	0	0	0			0
					1	0	0	0	0		+90
						0	0	0	0	0	180

Representing 00000100000 would be the successive run-of-five groups 00000, 00001, 00010, 00100, 01000, 10000, 00000. This results in the transmitter sending the QPSK pattern 180, +90, −90, −90, 0, +90, 180. Note that a continuous sequence of zeros (the idle sequence) gives continuous reversals, the same as BPSK.

5. VITERBI DECODING

Viterbi decoding is used on the receiving side. It consists of a whole bank of parallel encoders, each fed with one possible "guess" at the transmitted data sequence. The outputs of these parallel encoders are all compared with the received symbol stream. Each time a new symbol is received, the encoders need to add an extra bit to their sequence guesses and consider that the new bit might be a 0 or a 1. This doubles the number of sequence guesses, but a clever technique allows half of all the guessed sequences to be discarded as being less likely than the other half, and this means that the number of guesses being tracked stays constant. After a large number of symbols have been received, the chances of a wrong guess at the first symbol tends to zero, so the decoder can be pretty sure that the first bit was right and it can be fed to the output. In practice this means that the decoder always outputs decoded data bits some time after they have been received. The one-way delay in PSK31 is 25 bits (800 mS) which is long enough to make sure that the decoder has done a good job, but not so long that it introduces an unacceptable delay in displaying the received text.

6. BIBLIOGRAPHY

The "official" PSK31 Web site is **aintel.bi.ehu.es/psk3l.html**, operated by Eduardo Jacob, EA2BAJ. The PSK31 software program may be downloaded from this site.

Steve Ford, WB8IMY, "PSK31—Has RTTY's Replacement Arrived?" *QST*, May 1999, pp 41-41.

TECHNICAL DESCRIPTION: DOMINO

By Murray Greenman, ZL1BPU

Domino is the name given by the developers to a family of IFK coded coherent phase single tone MFSK keyed modes, using sequential tone-pairs in two alternate fields arranged as orthogonal but interleaved tone sets.

The name *ZL2AFP domino* is that given to this first software realization of these modes.

The main aim of domino is to provide a simple-to-use, but slick-to-operate, digital chat mode for HF, especially the lower bands (160/80/60/40/30m) where multipath is such a problem. It was designed for beginners with limited skills, and perhaps equipment with limited performance, especially in the drift and offset department.

DESCRIPTION

MFSK offers very good immunity to interference and ionospheric effects, and is also very sensitive. However, it has several disadvantages, which remain problems even with good FEC. These disadvantages make the MFSK modes unattractive to beginners and those wanting fast exchanges of information. The problems are:

- An extreme tuning accuracy requirement, for example 4 Hz on MFSK16 and less on THROB and MFSK8
- Low drift tolerance, typically ±4 Hz per minute
- Slow sync lock at start of transmission (seconds)
- Latencies introduced by the FEC process that reduce "slickness" (6 sec in MFSK16)
- Difficulty identifying a weak signal for tuning purposes, as the lowest or center tone needs to be found exactly.

This new family of domino modes attempts to address these disadvantages with varying levels of success, and some trade-offs. The specific measures employed (so far!) in domino are:

- Incremental Frequency Keying

IFK provides independence of tuning and tolerance of drift. The cost is increased errors (one error always means two errors). There are numerous IFK related error mechanisms that still require better understanding.

The IFK technique was invented by Steve Olney, VK2ZTO, and has been successfully employed on LF by Alberto, I2PHD, in the *JASON* program. This is its first ever deployment in an HF chat mode.

- Alternating Tone Sets

Two independent tone sets, used alternately, to provide very fast symbol synchronism. The alternation is very quickly detected as an odd-even component in the receiver FFT, and is much faster than the impulse response technique used in MFSK16. Sync lock-up time is well under one second. The cost is a waste of useful bandwidth.

- Orthogonal Tone Sets

Independent tone sets to provide very good ISI performance. The improvement noticed so far is mostly in the time domain. The tone sets are arranged so that ionospheric modulation products cannot easily spill from one possible tone position to another, or from one symbol to the next. This is done by double-spacing the tones and interleaving the tone sets. A paper by Tim Giles triggered this idea. There will be better ways to achieve this, perhaps using a tone pattern restriction rule as suggested to the authors by Nino IZ8BLY, rather than two separate tone sets.

- Tone Set Interleave

Interleaving the tone sets obviously considerably reduces the necessary bandwidth, but the cost is confusion at the receiver, where due to receiver tuning errors, the FFT cannot know from which tone set a particular tone comes. We get round this with a fudge factor, sending a unique non-printing character that is detected readily when the tone order is wrong.

- Character-based System

Two symbols are used to send each character. The domino design is character based, not a binary system or bit-based system such as PSK31 or MFSK16. Each pair of tones means a specific character. The Coquelet designers assert that 2-tone MFSK gives lower BER than other multi-symbol systems, and slightly better than binary systems.

- Low Symbol Rate

A low baud rate is used to defeat the effects of multi-path reception. The slowest mode, domino8, will easily handle 100ms of multi-path, making it useful under the absolute worst of NVIS conditions, as experience has shown.

- Reduced Character Set

A small character set is used (63 characters), to improve efficiency at low data rates. Even at 11 baud, the typing speed is 44 WPM.

- No FEC Coding

No FEC is used as the mode is reasonably robust without it.

PERFORMANCE

It is this combination of techniques that give this mode its unique character. The performance that results, while not stunning, and not without other problems, is never-the-less good.

IFK provides high tolerance of receiver drift and tuning offset. Unlike MFSK16, which requires a tuning accuracy of 4 Hz and a drift rate of less than 4 Hz per minute, thanks to IFK, domino will handle an offset of 200 Hz or more and drift of 200 Hz/minute, provided of course that the signal remains within the operating passband.

Because of the double-spaced and interleaved tones, and the low data rate, domino can handle about 100ms of multi-path error (by comparison RTTY copes with less than 5ms). Obviously, domino16 is more affected than the slower domino11 and the slowest domino8.

With a restricted character set and no FEC, a data rate of 44 WPM is achieved at a symbol rate of only 11.025 baud. This compensates for the reduced data bandwidth due to interleaved alternated symbol pairs (16 tones are used for only three data bits instead of four). The mode is sufficiently robust that FEC is not usually needed.

The insistent "falling" sound to the tones when idle or between words can identify IFK11, and tuning is easy.

MODE DEFINITION

Domino encompasses three modes, identical except for baud rate, speed and bandwidth. These are achieved primarily by changing the sound-card sampling rate to 8000, 11025 or 16000 samples/sec. It is realized that not all sound cards will support all three sampling rates, but this technique reduces receiver overhead, allowing the software to operate on quite slow computers.

Modulation

Multi-tone frequency shift keying, single tone coherent phase (CPMFSK), using 16 tones spaced 1T, but used as orthogonal fields of 8 tones spaced 2T, interleaved at a spacing of 1T.

Sync Modulation

Each 3-bit data octet is multiplied by two (shifted left), and summed with a symbol synchronous square wave at half the baud rate with values 0 and 1. This results in two orthogonal tone fields with 2T spacing in-field, and each tone is at least 1T and one symbol period spaced from any other tone.

Coding

Characters are incrementally coded in two successive 3-bit data octets representing a proprietary 6-bit character set. Each pair of octets is subtracted (using signed addition) from the corresponding coded octet (i.e. the previously transmitted octets) in the previous character, and the signed result of each octet is logically ANDed with 7 to keep it within range. (At the receiver each octet pair is added to the last decoded corresponding previous octet and ANDed with 7). The high octet is transmitted first. Thus, the increment is signed and 6 bit, based on subtracting the new uncoded character from the previous transmitted character.

Character Sync

Tone set order (character sync) is recovered at the receiver from data context. This is possible because frequently used characters have unused equivalents when viewed with octets swapped. A special idle character is sent every 16 characters, making the reversal more obvious.

Necessary Bandwidth

Using the ITU definition, the necessary bandwidths for the modes domino8, domino11 and domino16, with symbol rates of 7.8125, 11.025 and 15.625 baud, are 158, 223 and 316Hz respectively. (45 baud RTTY rates 453Hz)

The formula used for MFSK mode bandwidth calculation is $BW = B + msk$ where B = baud rate, m is the number of tones, and s is the tone spacing. k is a factor related to keying technique, and $k = 1.2$ for coherent phase keying.

ITU Emission Designator

The mode is single channel subcarrier modulated SSB transmitted automatically received data, so rates as J2B. Hence, the modes are classified as 158HJ2B, 223HJ2B and 316HJ2B. (By the way, the last of these is identical in designator and bandwidth to MFSK16, while RTTY rates 450HJ2B). Emission Designators are outlined in FCC Part 47 Rules, para. 2.201.

Index

FEEDBACK

Please use this form to give us your comments on this book and what you'd like to see in future editions, or e-mail us at **pubsfdbk@arrl.org** (publications feedback). If you use e-mail, please include your name, call, e-mail address and the book title, edition and printing in the body of your message. Also indicate whether or not you are an ARRL member.

Where did you purchase this book?
☐ From ARRL directly   ☐ From an ARRL dealer

Is there a dealer who carries ARRL publications within:
☐ 5 miles   ☐ 15 miles   ☐ 30 miles   of your location?   ☐ Not sure.

License class:
☐ Novice   ☐ Technician   ☐ Technician Plus   ☐ General   ☐ Advanced   ☐ Extra

---

Name _____

ARRL member?   ☐ Yes ☐ No
Call Sign _____

Daytime Phone (   ) _____   Age _____

Address _____

City, State/Province, ZIP/Postal Code _____

If licensed, how long? _____   E-mail _____

Other hobbies _____

_____

Occupation _____

For ARRL use only	HF DIG
Edition	3 4 5 6 7 8 9 10 11 12
Printing	2 3 4 5 6 7 8 9 10 11 12

From _____

_____

_____

EDITOR, HF DIGITAL HANDBOOK
ARRL—THE NATIONAL ASSOCIATION FOR AMATEUR RADIO
225 MAIN STREET
NEWINGTON CT 06111-1494

— — — — — — — — — — — please fold and tape — — — — — — — — — — — — —